Jacopone

Brother Ramon SSF studied theology in Cardiff, Zürich and Edinburgh, has been a parish priest and university chaplain, and is a member of the Anglican Society of Saint Francis.

As Guardian of the SSF House of Prayer at Glasshampton, Worcestershire, he has written extensively on the life of prayer and spirituality. He is currently exploring the hermit life.

**Books available from Collins Religious Publishing
by the same author**

*A HIDDEN FIRE
DEEPER INTO GOD
FULNESS OF JOY
HEAVEN ON EARTH
SOUL FRIENDS*

In the Christian Spirituality Series:

*LIFE'S CHANGING SEASONS
PRAYING THE BIBLE
PRAYING THE JESUS PRAYER
REMEMBER ME*

JACOPONE

by
Brother Ramon SSF

Collins
FLAME

William Collins Sons & Co. Ltd.
London · Glasgow · Sydney · Auckland
Toronto · Johannesburg

First Published in Great Britain in 1990 by Flame

Flame is an imprint of
Collins Religious Division
part of the Collins Publishing Group
8 Grafton Street, London W1X 3LA

Printed and Bound by Bell and Bain Ltd., Glasgow

CONDITIONS OF SALE

To my dear sister
Wendy
with love

and the Turner family
Mike
Paul
Karen
Nicola
Lee

and in memory of J

CONTENTS

BIOGRAPHICAL NOTE OF JACOPONE DA TODI
(1230 – 1306)

Jacopone was born in Todi about 1230 of an aristocratic family when Umbrian Italy, together with other Italian provinces, was experiencing economic and cultural revival.

After studying law in Bologna he married Vanna di Bernardino di Guidone, a beautiful woman with Franciscan penitent sympathies. Jacopone was then thirty-eight years old and settling into the life of a *notaio*, which included law and accountancy.

After just a year of marriage Vanna fell to her death from a balcony at a social function to which Jacopone had taken her. This completely turned his mind and heart and he became a *bizocone*, a ragged Franciscan penitent, and wandered around Umbria for ten years, sometimes deranged, sometimes prophetically powerful in word and life, but unacceptable to the Conventual friars of Todi who fought shy of his extravagances. Many of his penitential and meditative poems date from this period and he gained a reputation for holiness and asceticism, though in his own strange style.

In 1278, while the controversy between the Conventual and Spiritual Franciscans was intense, Jacopone was accepted at the Todi friary, though his sympathies were with the Spirituals. His devotion to Christ and holy poverty gave rise to more poetic writing and itinerant preaching, and the emphasis of his spirituality during this period became less ascetic and more mystical.

In July 1294, after more than two years of violent disagreement and intrigue among the cardinals, Pietro da Morrone, the hermit of Abbruzzi was elected pope. This heartened many Spirituals though Jacopone became increasingly sceptical of the outcome.

In spite of his misgivings, together with other Spirituals, he appealed to the new pope, now Celestine V, and obtained protection against the persecuting Conventuals. But his doubts as to the ability of Celestine to stand against insidious corruption and political intrigue were justified. Five months after his coronation, Celestine V abdicated, and the principal villain (in Jacopone's eyes), ascended the throne of Peter as Boniface VIII in December 1294. Jacopone denied the validity of Celestine's abdication and Boniface's election, holding Bonifíce to be Antichrist.

The poems of this period include lamentations on the Church and apocalyptic threats; warnings to Celestine on his accession and attacks and pleas addressed to Boniface, including also some poems of profound spiritual darkness and vision.

In signing the Longhezza Manifesto of 1297, Jacopone and other Spirituals threw in their lot with the Colonna Cardinals in their rebellion against Boniface. Jacopone's denial of the validity of Boniface's election officially broke his Franciscan obedience to the papacy in the eyes of the Conventuals. Boniface soon put down the rebellion, captured Jacopone and condemned him to life imprisonment with excommunication in an underground cell in Palestrina.

Boniface ignored his repeated pleas for mercy and pardon, and Jacopone went through phases of misery, spiritual darkness and the dawning of mystical light and union with God.

In 1303 Boniface was captured by French forces at Anagni and soon died. Jacopone was then released by his successor, Benedict XI, and spent his last three years with the friars of Collazzone near Todi. He died on Christmas Eve 1306 in the Poor Clare convent at Collazzone, ten years after the death of Celestine, and three years after that of Boniface VIII.

It was during the last decade of his life that he underwent dramatic spiritual transformation through the darkness and pain of spiritual death and rebirth. He reveals in his life and poetry a particularly Franciscan manifestation of the mystical stages of purgation, illumination and union with God. This is clearly Christ-centred rather than platonic and speaks from the depths of his humanity and living experience.

Jacopone was a man of depths and heights — given to extremes. His life and writings have been a source both of acute embarrassment to the Church and of sheer delight to those who are seeking a closer walk with God in the fellowship of Christ.

Ramon SSF
The Society of St Francis

Part One

1 Dark Night of the Soul

Jacopone, the Franciscan friar from Todi, lay in his stinking underground cell in the dungeons beneath the ruined fortress of Palestrina. The place was thick with the smell of human excrement. Water trickled through the mould on the walls. A stout metal door was set in one wall and a small grille, admitting a square of light, in the other.

His fetters had chafed his wrists and ankles to the bone and his food consisted of scraps of leftovers and crusts — if the rats did not get there first. The nights were cold even though it was only September, in the year 1298. What would it be like when winter set in?

Jacopone allowed himself a grim smile as he recalled the pope's wrath which had issued in his excommunication and imprisonment. He had been captured when Boniface VIII's troops had finally broken into the Colonna fortress in Palestrina, taking all the insurrectionists prisoner. Jacopone, special target, had been dragged off separately, to Rome to face the pope who had been waiting for this moment.

"So, Jacopone!" cried Boniface, resplendent in his white papal robe, with oiled and scented hair and beard, looking with contempt on Jacopone's bedraggled and exhausted condition. "What do you have to say to me now?"

The pope had been hoping for penitence, remorse and submission, but he was faced with a stubborn and unrepentant prisoner. "Only what you have already heard from our true pope Celestine before his untimely death at your hands", retorted Jacopone. "You crept in like a fox, you reign like a lion and you will die like a dog — you fork-tongued Antichrist!"

Boniface was incensed. His face became contorted and his

breathing rapid as he jabbed his finger menacingly at Jacopone's chest. "And I'll tell you what I have to say to *you*. . ." he spluttered, trying to control his trembling.

He stood up on his feet and summoned what appearance of authority he could muster. Then he cried out: "Jacopone, you are excommunicate from Christ, cut off from the sacraments of the Church, and you will suffer perpetual imprisonment beneath the ruined site of that very fortress from which you defied me."

A black and cold horror took hold of Jacopone at these words. But he stood his ground, looking into the face of Boniface with courage and scorn — uttering no further word.

He shivered now, both with the memory and with the cold of this morning, and reflected on the events which had brought him to his present sorry state.

Four years previously, in July 1294, after more than two years of delay and intrigue among the cardinals after the death of Nicholas IV, and as a result of an apocalyptic letter from Pietro da Morrone the Abruzzi hermit, they had elected the hermit pope.

One of the participating cardinals, Benedetto Gaetani of the Orsini family, had watched the proceedings with keen interest. Jacopone suspected him of manipulating affairs behind the scenes. Gaetani wanted the papal chair for himself but his political intriguing was too well known and he could not hope for election at that moment. A stop-gap was needed.

Jacopone's sympathies lay with the Colonna faction of cardinals who were the supporters of the *zelanti* or Spiritual Franciscans, and although he had joined the *mitigati* or Conventual Franciscans in Todi, yet his heart was with the *zelanti* party.

For the moment Gaetani's Orsini faction and the Colonna faction were united in the election of the hermit Pietro da Morrone to become Pope Celestine V.

The Spiritual Franciscans were immediately elated because a saintly hermit had been elected pope. But Jacopone was sceptical of the outcome. He and Benedetto Gaetani were both from Todi, from opposing families but sharing a powerful antipathy towards each other from boyhood. They had both received a legal training and both had showed an arrogant and ambitious cast of mind.

Gaetani had never deviated from his ambitious path over the years; but Jacopone had undergone bereavement, near-madness and conversion to God since those early days.

Eventually Gaetani had become a cardinal, with the help of his uncle, and Jacopone suspected him of having his eye on the papal chair. The election of the hermit was part of a larger plan.

Jacopone's suspicions were confirmed. Pietro, as Celestine V, lasted only five months as pope, unable to stand against the corruption and cunning of the papal court. Gaetani was on hand to help Celestine towards abdication because of his "inability and unworthiness", and Gaetani himself ascended the papal throne as Boniface VIII in December 1294.

Jacopone and the Spiritual Franciscans denied the validity of the abdication and Boniface's election, holding him to be Antichrist. Jacopone groaned now in his prison cell as he recalled the clear change of direction in his pilgrimage which this event had brought about. He had turned from the path of spiritual preaching and prayer to political intrigue and insurrection.

In 1297, together with two *zelanti* friars, he signed the Longhezza Manifesto, throwing in his lot with the Colonna brother cardinals and some French prelates. This manifesto denied the validity of Boniface's election, thereby declaring him anti-pope. Boniface violently put down the rebellion, sentencing Jacopone to excommunication and perpetual imprisonment under the now devastated Colonna fortress at Palestrina. So here he was!

The strange thing was that Jacopone could appreciate his situation with a certain ironic satisfaction. Lying shivering and hungry this early morning, he had plenty of time to reflect on his predicament. His currying favour with political groups in

Rome, his partisan enlistment with the Colonna and French prelates and his equivocal and over-righteous indignation at the evils of Boniface had landed him here.

There was more objectivity and clarity in his cell-thinking than had ever been possible in his espousal of violence. Jesus had said: "They that take the sword shall perish with the sword", and neither he nor Francis had ever deviated from that principle. But Jacopone had. And yet he had been delivered!

He even found himself thinking more sympathetically about Benedetto Gaetani sitting on his papal throne as Boniface VIII. Jacopone wondered at the grace which had intervened to save him from himself, and he felt sorry for Boniface who had achieved his ambitions but sat insecurely on the throne, claiming more than any pope before him, with increasing troubles challenging him both spiritually and temporally. So much for the two-tiered papal tiara which Boniface had invented to symbolize his spiritual and secular powers.

"If God's grace had not intervened where should I be now?" pondered Jacopone. 'I might have perished in my sin or I might have achieved worldly glory in my own way — but I would not have been granted this opportunity for repentance — even though in a freezing and stinking prison cell!"

He did have some anxiety as to how long this state of euphoria would last — but just now he was counting his blessings. By his arrest and imprisonment he had been prevented from continuing on the path of iconoclasm and revenge, and he knew that the more he had persisted in that way the fainter would have become his awareness of the divine Love, and the less he would have been able to respond to all that Brother John of La Verna had meant to him.

The memory of John caused him to wince with painful longing. How could they have drifted apart like this? — though it was Jacopone who had done the drifting. He thought of their first time together on mount La Verna in Tuscany, when the young John had undergone both ecstasy and desolation and Jacopone had helped him through his dark night of the soul.

Together they had learned some of the secrets of the mystical life to which they believed they had been called.

They had pored over the writings of the fathers of the desert, of John Cassian, Dionysius the Areopagite and other spiritual writings which Guardian Mario had fed to them.

With almost thirty years' difference between them, they had been of one mind and one heart. Their love for Christ sharpened and deepened their love for each other, and during times of separation when Jacopone had been recalled to Todi, went out on preaching missions or spent times in solitude alone and then with groups of *zelanti* hermits, there had been a quality of immediacy in their awareness of each other's love and prayer.

That had gone on for years. But as Jacopone, through his work for Cardinal Bentivenga in Rome, had become more interested and fascinated by political and ecclesiastical intrigues, he had frequented La Verna less. He had become busy, involved, immersed in the life and work which called forth his literary and oratorical talents — and he had become popular in those circles.

Almost imperceptibly the mystical life represented by John had faded, and because of his neglect the immediacy of John's love and prayers had been allowed to take second and then third place. Then it had all but faded completely. In any case it was easier, more convenient, less painful not to think of John and La Verna as he sided with the anti-papal party. There was a certain incompatibility about the two ways — though Jacopone had not actually admitted that at the time.

He did a quick calculation and said to himself: "John is now the age I was when my dear Vanna fell to her death and I was ushered into madness and conversion to God. All these thirty years he has been growing in love through darkness and glory, into ever-increasing union with God."

He found himself weeping quietly at the thought of the wasted years of confrontation and militant opposition to anything that "the great Jacopone" did not see as the primitive

Franciscan vision. "And all the time it was *my* vision," he whispered, "and *my* pattern."

He remembered his own self-will and desire for attention and prestige in his early zealous preaching around Umbria when Alberto, the Guardian of the Todi convent, had tried to lead him in the way of moderation and humility.

Then his mind carried him down to the Portiuncula below Assisi, where Brothers Leo and Rufino, the original companions of St Francis, had communicated to him their primitive Franciscan vision.

"I listened and partly obeyed," mused Jacopone, "but my former arrogance and pride had not really died. It simply lay dormant.

"Then I met John when he was young, enthused and inebriated with the love of God. He, more than anyone else, showed me the love of Christ. How can I for so long have cut myself off from such a precious friendship? How I miss him, and how clearly I see these things now! But is it too late?"

He groaned and turned over on his wooden pallet, the chains cutting still more his bruised and aching legs.

During the first weeks of his imprisonment he tried to keep alive his sense of humour. There were times in the first warmer days of October when he was not too cold, that he thought of himself being penned in like a pig to be fattened for the festive season. He wrote some lines about it:

Though day and night penned in I lie,
A fattening pig within his sty,
I fear the Christmas is not nigh
When they will make good pork of me.

"If the friars searching for bishoprics were put on to my diet," he told himself with a chuckle one evening, "they'd shorten their sermons for want of strength and breath."

As he said this he looked up at the small basket hanging from the beam, which had been procured for him by the rough, though not too unfriendly, jailer. Jacopone's reputation counted for something with him for he traded his prisoner a crust or a piece of left-over fish for two or three Paternosters, hoping that a good word from Jacopone to the Lord would stand him in good stead on the day of judgment.

It was through this jailer that Jacopone occasionally smuggled out poems and notes to *zelanti* groups in Rome and beyond, and this small means of communication sustained him when darker days came. And come they did.

First of all it was the matter of excommunication. Jacopone hardly knew what to think now about the validity of Boniface's election, for he had heard that the good friar Peter Olivi had argued that if abdication were not possible then even a heretic pope could not be got rid of. Bad pope Boniface certainly was, in a moral and spiritual sense, but Jacopone knew that the grace and validity of the priestly office did not depend upon the holiness of the priest. Might that not also be true of the pope?

Jacopone's excommunication was a sore trial to him. With all the Franciscan mystics he found that his love and adoration for Christ was centred in Holy Communion. They had taken from him his habit also, and though his spiritual life did not depend upon that, yet it symbolized for him the corporate life of his Order. Even Scripture and breviary had been denied him, though he was negotiating with his jailer for a breviary to be smuggled in.

Fortunately he knew the psalter by heart and could repeat many Bible passages from memory. But all this lack of spiritual food and fellowship, together with the incarceration from fresh air, fields and mountains, drew him down into depression and darkness as November gave way to the colder months of winter.

In his early ascetic period following his conversion, he had written many poems requesting cold, deprivation, sickness and even pain. But that had been twenty and thirty years before. He was now moving towards his seventieth year and things looked and felt very different. He remembered that his Guardian, Alberto, used to say that life's asceticisms were sufficient without flagellation and other self-imposed penances. How right he was!

Alberto. It was from him that a greasy and somewhat tattered parchment arrived some months later when Jacopone was feeling particularly low. The effect of his words was the kindling of a spark of hope within Jacopone's soul, and he read them with tears of gratitude:

> My dearly beloved Jacopo: Nothing has happened to you that I have not learned. You are constantly within my mind and heart, and therefore within my prayers. You remain a brother of this convent and I care for you as my beloved son though we are of the same age. May I remind you that you once believed that you had been called to the fulfilment of a vision and a task. You have only partially fulfilled either and both vision and task await your completion.
>
> Learn what you have to in your present darkness, my brother, for you can sink to no depth that Christ has not plumbed before you, and can know no desolation of which He has not drunk more deeply.
>
> In the fullness of time, be it brief or long, you will be drawn up out of the pit as was the prophet Jeremiah, and you will know renewal of vision and strength of heart and will to complete the task in love.
>
> I believe this note will reach you as a token of our Lord's mercy and grace.
>
> Your Guardian and brother, Alberto.

Jacopone pondered upon the implications of such a letter. Alberto evidently did not take the excommunication seriously, wrote no word of harsh criticism, but communicated only love and hope. There was no date upon the note but it had been through greasy and dirty hands.

It would not be true to say that hope irradiated Jacopone's soul but certainly there was a spark kindled with Alberto's words, by means of which purgation gave way to illumination and hope.

Jacopone memorized the contents and tore the thin parchment into fragments, hiding it with the grasses in the latrine which opened into his cell. He was used to the foul smell now, just as he knew himself to be infested with lice and vermin in addition to all his other tribulations.

The Colonna brothers did not come near him, fearing any compromise which would bring retribution upon them. They had lost their purple but had outwardly submitted to Boniface, though that was not the end of the matter. The two *zelanti* brothers, Benedetto and Deodato, who had signed the Longhezza Manifesto with Jacopone, had been imprisoned elsewhere and he did not know how they fared.

One day towards the end of the year 1299, his jailer said something that made Jacopone's heart leap. He mentioned the General Indulgence offered during the Papal Jubilee.

"What do you mean?" questioned Jacopone.

"The pope is extending pardon to prisoners and forgiveness to repentant sinners under the ban, to celebrate the year 1300, and his illustrious pontificate," said the jailer, not without some irony. He was always careful what he said though the manner of his speech was significant to the hearer.

The news filled Jacopone with excitement. "Here is a way for the pope to grant a lifting of the ban, even the possibility of release, without losing face," he thought. So he set his mind to composing a form of words which would indicate a certain humility, if not penitence.

The jailer (in exchange for some fervent prayers) brought writing materials and Jacopone set his mind to the task, laying aside his former objections for the sake of the lifting of the excommunication:

Pope Boniface, you have anathematized and
    excommunicated me;
Will you not now absolve and heal me?
There are many weapons you may still use against me,
Let not excommunication be the chief of them.

I have two shields against adversaries,
Self-hatred on the left, love of enemies on the right;
Come near to me and feel the heat of these shields,
No longer pierce me with the mortal wound of the ban.

I am like a sheep bleating outside the sheepfold,
Act as true Pastor and restore me to the fold;
I am like the blind man crying "Mercy" to the Saviour,
And like the paralytic racked with pain.

The pool of Bethesda has been moved with many pardons,
But there is no-one to lower me into its healing waters;
I am stinking and corrupt in my pigsty,
Speak the word of cleansing and release.

I lie in death like the daughter of Jairus,
Take my hand and lead me back to Francis' table;
The members of my Order weep for me
As I totter on the brink of hell.

I am four days in the fetid tomb,
With no Martha or Mary to intercede;
With authority, say: "Lazarus, come forth,"
That I may be once more son and brother.

It did not a scrap of good. One, two, three appeals passed from
Jacopone to Boniface but no notice was taken of any. The year
of Jubilee came and went — Jacopone's seventieth year. But still
he languished in prison. Darkness fell upon him — the dark
night of the soul.

The strange thing in all this was that there seemed to be some
small space or dimension of soul, glimpsed only momentarily,
with no effort or hope on Jacopone's part, when he could see,
feel, touch — what analogy could be used? — the presence of
love.

It did not lessen his conflict or lighten his darkness; it did not
alleviate his sufferings or lift his burdens — but it was there! And
it prevented him from sinking into utter despair. It bided its

time, seemingly knowing that all the ground of self-love must be broken up and all hope must be abandoned — save hope in God.

Jacopone felt that he had been in conflict with Satan through many years and had won victory after victory by the grace of God. He had confronted both the opposition and the adoration of his fellows and had found at last the way of victory through defeat. But *this* battle was one of self-revelation, learning the lesson of self-naughting, placing no faith or hope any longer in the inebriation of joy or *jubilus*. Nor yet in grief, penitence or worldly wisdom. It was the way of total abandonment, of purgation of spirit, which drew him at last to the very edge of the abyss.

As these painful lessons were being learned at a level never before experienced, Jacopone began to feel a strange detachment from anxiety and a new objectivity of spirit that held him in a manner entirely new. He wrote no more letters to Pope Boniface, and the matter of excommunication was no longer one for concern.

He felt himself being drawn more profoundly into his own depths. He did not now say prayers so much as dwell deep in silence. Sometimes it was akin to breathless adoration and at other times it was accompanied by an overflow of tears, gratitude and penitence.

But all the time he was held. There was a co-operative passivity on his part and a willingness to be carried back over the years. He was immersed in the depths and lifted to the heights, but always with a gentleness that did no violence to his sensitive and vulnerable spirit.

It was an interior journey undertaken from the stillness of his cell, but one which brought him back full circle, to the present moment of waiting — and of darkness before dawn.

2   Beloved Vanna

There was no doubt that physically Jacopone was a prisoner. The darkness, the cold, the pain, the hunger, the filth and the vermin were evidence enough! But when his spirit went roaming over the past years of his life he felt free of his body — liberated to wander in thought and spirit down the years, to learn again at an ever-deeper level the lessons of pain and ecstasy — joy and sorrow mingling in the sunshine and shadow of his experience of life and of God.

Sometimes he would induce within himself a free-floating reminiscence which would carry him away from the present cramping coldness and pain of his prison.

But one evening, after even the small square of light at the wall grille had been lost in the darkness and the wretched meal of dried crust, watery broth and stale onion was over, he lay on his board and was carried away to childhood. Words came back to him which he had written about the tenderness of his mother getting up in the night to answer his crying:

> She, seeing that I suffered from some ill,
>   All trembling still,
>   And fearing I must die,
> Would light her little lamp with tender thrill,
> Turn down the coverlet, and gaze her fill,
>   Seeing me sleeping lie.
>   And for my cry
> No evil cause she sees;
>   She heaves a sigh,
> Her heart may be at ease.

The child grew up stubborn and wayward, as he remembered. Full of energy and hating all discipline, he found education boring and often earned his father's thrashings. His independent and arrogant spirit he traced back to the street fighting of boyhood, alive with an intensity and pugnacity which prepared him for future battles with bishops and pope!

As he reached the age of sixteen and seventeen his boyhood battles gave way to student vendettas at the university of Bologna. But now he began to appreciate the aesthetic pleasures of creativity and beauty, of good food, music and poetry.

Bologna's university was second in Europe at that time, only excelled by Paris, and as Jacopone studied logic, literature, philosophy and law he came into contact with the new poetry which captured his imagination, bringing heart and mind into bondage and stirring up an inward restlessness.

Stirred by such memories, the old man began whispering to himself "Bologna and law," he muttered, "and what for? I wanted money, luxury, reputation, and the adventures I lacked I invented and boasted of them to my fellows to cover the emptiness within.

"And why didn't I use those accommodating women of Bologna? God knows I wanted them, and my friends talked enough about their own exploits. I did not love chastity, but there was a fear of disease in the whorehouses and brothels of Bologna.

"My mind and body certainly lusted after every beautiful woman — and some not so beautiful — and yet I knew that I would only turn in revulsion from a night of lust. And perhaps I was waiting for Vanna!"

Jacopone suddenly saw her face in vision as he twisted on his prison pallet. "Vanna! You come to me now as you came to me one day in the streets of Todi. By that time I had become a lawyer, a notary — and a usurer into the bargain. I was caught in the web of my own conceit and avarice, but one look from you stirred up deep yearnings in my arrogant soul.

"How long I watched you from a distance, not knowing how to approach you! You were as elusive as a butterfly — and as beautiful. How could I hope to catch you, entangle you and draw you to myself? You despised arrogance, cared nothing for my reputation and I couldn't bribe you by wealth or social distinction.

"Then came that day when I looked upon you and was astonished at my weakness. I gazed at you and my world crumbled. I lay awake that night and knew wretchedness and hope, yearning and tears — and all for your sake!

"And you remember that day, don't you, Vanna? Suddenly, unexpectedly for both of us, we met face to face. You turned your eyes away as I looked at you. I planted my feet firmly, refusing to let you pass — but you stood your ground! You come to me now and I hear the music of your voice as I heard it then and as it sounded during the brief months of our marriage."

He felt the gentle breathing of Vanna upon his cheek, and seemed to hear her voice. "Yes Jacopo. I suddenly saw you before me when you returned to Todi. You were far beyond me. You were too violent and worldly for me — and too learned! Your fastidiousness, arrogance and ambition I despised. But there was something in your eyes, in your soul, that drew me to you and kept me waiting for you, even as a young girl.

"I was in love with you. But how can I say it? — I was in love with God too. You never understood that then, but after my death you understood. It was difficult for me to separate my love for God from my love for you — as if in loving Him I loved you more. And only by love could you be won. So I gave myself to you — love for love. But I did not cease to pray, and I believed that love would answer love in your heart."

Perspiration stood on Jacopone's brow in spite of the cold. His heart beat wildly as his vision was filled with the beauty of Vanna, the eighteen-year-old girl with black, braided hair, liquid brown eyes, olive skin and a slimness of breast and waist that made him catch his breath. His lips moved, though his words were not audible.

"Ah yes, my Vanna. You knew even then. You understood that my reputation for violence, my gambling and my mounting debts and all my passion for exuberant life and power were because I thirsted for love. You saw past my vanity and arrogance, my conceit of dress and manner. You saw, even in the wild stories of my duels and vendettas, the enthusiasm for life and love that yearned and was forever unsatisfied — until we met that day in the street and my world began to fall about my ears."

He felt the touch of Vanna's hand on his forehead and heart. She spoke gently to him: "I could not explain the effect of your love to myself, Jacopo, let alone to you. It was as if God's love shone through you — and I had despised and loved you from afar since I had been a young girl. I had long felt the radiance of God's love in St Francis — and that I could understand — but then it shone through you!"

Jacopone sighed. "How strange I found it that so many of the young men and women of Todi were moved and challenged by asceticism. My love of comfort and good eating blinded me to the quest and adventure that called the penitents to follow the music of Francis of Assisi.

"I did not know that you too had been caught up in that movement, until you declared your love for me. I despised those emotional processions of flagellants who roamed through the Umbrian towns with their singing and wailing. I believed that the young Franciscan hermit Ranieri stole the hearts of many a woman through his ascetic beauty and erotic charm. I was jealous for you, Vanna. But what did I know of penitence and faith? What did I care for the crucified Jesus and the way of the cross? It was in you that I saw love in human form. Your beauty lifted me into realms of hope and joy. Your loveliness assuaged my thirst and caused me to feel that without you my heart was a dry and arid desert."

Vanna smiled and reminded him again of their encounter. "When you stood before me in the street and barred my way I did not give way to you. I lifted my head boldly and looked into your eyes — and even anticipated the declaration of your love. But I was trembling inside. Was this the moment of your change of heart, Jacopo? Did you hide it from me, allowing it to emerge from the depths of your soul when it burst forth at my death?"

Vanna's words seemed to have reverberated in Jacopone's unconscious depths, becoming clear in his reverie as he shivered in his cell. He was not now aware of his surroundings, for he was back again reliving the events which surrounded that awful tragedy.

"Your death! Oh Vanna, that day is engraved upon my heart. Less than a year of marriage — many times I have longed to live those months again! I was irreligious and ambitious, hedonistic and selfish. I loved refinement in music and poetry but had no love for God. And all the time you were patient and loving. When I would not allow you to speak of the love of God you never ceased to pray for me. In obedience you allowed me to dress you in magnificent garments to display my arrogance in a beautiful wife. And yet I loved you tenderly, as you did me. That day of the public festival in Todi was one such day of pride and conceit for me.

"I was determined that you would be admired and I would be envied as I took you to the celebration. I surrounded myself with admirers while you wandered up to the balcony of the house where the dancers were assembled. I remember well the sudden collapse of the structure, the cries and screams of the people — and I knew that you were among them. Frantically I rushed to the wreckage, searching and calling your name. At last I found you — and ignored the moaning of the injured people around you in my struggle to lift the wooden beam that had pinned you to the ground. Panic filled my mind and a strange presentiment of death flooded my heart — others were injured, but you were dead!"

"It's all over now Jacopo. I am at peace, and soon you will enter into blessedness. But that tragedy was the beginning of salvation, and madness, for you. Was it there among the debris, or when you had my body taken home, that you discovered the hair shirt beneath my showy clothes? That was when you fully realized the depth of my penitence and the longing of my heart for your salvation."

"I was astonished and terrified. If this was my wife then I had never known her! All this time you had been praying for me, doing penance for my sins, leading me to the love of God. And at last you succeeded — at the cost of your life. My beautiful wife had been an ascetic. You, not I, were the lover. I had never truly loved or understood the meaning of it all."

Vanna's voice came again: "That was a long time ago, Jacopo. Then began your holy madness — caused by the death of the sweet and docile wife you had never known. And yet you did know me. Perhaps on that day you began to love me truly and we began to love one another in God. That was the beginning of your new life in Christ. I think, my beloved Jacopo, that you could never have learned to love utterly unless you had lost me in death. You needed darkness, loneliness and death to recognize the path of love. Perhaps that, too, was the will of God."

Jacopone groaned and stirred upon his prison pallet. This was the first of many episodes of his life which would unfold before him in the underground dungeon of Palestrina, a prisoner of the pope, excommunicate and without hope or promise of release.

He returned again to his own depths, entering into the strange melancholy and madness that had laid hold of him on the day of Vanna's death; and one of the stanzas from his own *Laude* murmured itself in his soul:

Weep, eyes of mine, and mourn,
    Cease not to weep and pray;
Repent, and Love will turn
    Your anguish to allay.
So fierce my thirst now burns,
    It wastes my heart away,
For Christ, my Dawn, my Day,
    For Christ who is my Love.

3   Holy Madness

Vanna's body lay on the couch. The bodice was untied, exposing the penitent hair shirt. All efforts to revive her under the collapsed balcony had failed and Jacopone hardly remembered the journey home as he held her body in the carriage. His tears and cries mingled with the shouts of curious onlookers who had heard the news and came running behind the carriage to Jacopone's home in Todi.

The physician had come and gone. The priest was due at any moment to say the prayers for the departed soul. It was too late for extreme unction or for the last sacrament to help Vanna on her way into eternity. Jacopone had insisted on bringing her home before a priest could be found.

He felt a strange numbness claiming his whole body. His throat was constricted and a band of pain across his chest hardly allowed him to breathe. His pulse had become faint and feeble and cold sweat was upon his brow and the palms of his hands. For a few moments he struggled for breath and then a shuddering sobbing overtook him, the like of which he had not known before.

It was in this condition that the priest found him, accompanied by the matron who was to wash and lay out the cold body of the beautiful woman who had been Jacopone's wife for just a year. Jacopone was on his knees, his head upon Vanna's bosom, his tears soaking her bodice and the hair shirt which had devastated him when he first saw it, an hour or so before.

Father Salvatore, a Dominican priest who served one of the fashionable churches in Todi, tried to silence Jacopone while he recited the prayers. "Come now Jacopo," he said in a low voice, trying to lift him to his feet. "Take hold of yourself for Vanna's sake and for your own."

But Jacopone would not be levered up from his kneeling position, so Father Salvatore began to recite the prayers while the matron knelt the other side of Jacopone, quietly sharing in his weeping:

> *Requiem aeternam dona ei, Domine: Et lux perpetua luceat ei.*
> Rest eternal grant unto her, O Lord: and let light perpetual shine upon her . . .

When the prayers were finished Jacopone let himself be led into the next room by Mama Lucia. A strange sort of passivity held him, alternating with shivering and trembling. But he did not say a word. Over the next few days he seemed not to be able to respond to outward happenings. He was taken to the funeral and sat dazed in the chapel during the requiem mass. Then later, in the cemetery, he swayed while the body was being lowered into the grave, falling upon the ground as the priest intoned the words of committal and the final blessing.

For three days he lay inert while Mama Lucia organized two of her domestic girls to care for him — reporting each evening on his condition. On the morning of the third day the girl Julia found his bed linen scattered over the floor, the back door of the house open and Jacopone gone. Father Salvatore, the physician and Jacopone's brother Frederick were sent for, and a hasty search was organized. for the whole neighbourhood was sensitive to the dumb grief which had paralysed Jacopone since Vanna's death.

Three of the town lads made for the cemetery where they found the distraught lawyer half naked, covered with earth and mud, moaning prostrate over Vanna's fresh grave and bleeding where he had cut himself with stones. The lads were horrified and scared to go near him. Two of them ran back to tell the others while the third stood by apprehensive and afraid lest Jacopone should become violent or hysterical.

Many of the townspeople gathered at the gate of the cemetery while two of Jacopone's former friends went up to him. Murmuring gently, consoling and helping him, supporting his weight between them, they stood with him for a time while he continued his low moans, spittle and blood running down the stubble of his face which, until now, had been carefully shaved each day.

Eventually the news of his condition reached Frederick's ears and he coaxed and led Jacopone down to his modest home in Todi. Frederick was a stonemason and had hitherto not been close to his brother because Jacopone had first spent a great deal of the family money on his education in Bologna and then gambled and wasted money when he returned, before becoming the fastidious and arrogant lawyer that he had been up to the time of Vanna's death.

But this was forgotten now as Frederick took Jacopone's arm. "Stay with us," he urged. "I know you hate being dependent, Jacopo, but I can't leave you alone in that empty house while the rest of the family are warmed and fed here."

But Jacopone would not stay, would not talk, would not communicate. Mama Lucia and her two girls took him in hand again. Under their care he slowly began to take food, and his behaviour settled down into a pattern of weeping, wandering up to the cemetery above the chapel and avoiding other human contact.

So began the months during which the people of Todi grew used to the radical change in Jacopone's behaviour. They attributed it to the devastation of soul which had overtaken him in the tragedy of Vanna's death, and they were partly right. What they could not see was the inner transformation which was taking place in his mind and heart as a consequence of the discovery of the depth of Vanna's faith and love for God.

The folk of Todi were almost lulled into indifference during those months. But soon they were stirred with great curiosity and even incredulity by the symptons of either madness of prophetic symbolism that were manifested when Jacopone began to reach out in communicative gestures and language which needed some interpretation.

It began with a discovery which Jacopone made one day while searching among Vanna's belongings. He came across a sheaf of parchments written in her careful handwriting. His heart leaped as he saw the pages, for they had exchanged letters, notes and poems which were full of tenderness and love. And now here was the precious handwriting again.

He took the manuscript over to his bed and knelt down to examine it. The sight of it, worn and tear-stained, the touch and smell of it, brought Vanna before him. It contained her meditations on the life of St Francis, copied partly from the legends which circulated around Umbria and the Marches of Ancona and partly from the writings of Thomas of Celano.

Apart from Holy Scripture and her diligent attendance at mass, here were the roots of Vanna's spiritual life. She seemed to have woven a tapestry of her own meditations out of the material provided from Church homilies, legendary stories, the "people who knew people who knew Francis" and the *zelanti* friars who lived in hill hermitages and old Franciscan sites away from the convents of the respectable *mitigati* friars such as those who lived in Todi itself. Jacopone's eyes fell on the place which recorded Francis' answering the bells and trumpets of Assisi in November 1202, when the city called upon its menfolk to defend it against the Perugians. Vanna's hand continued the story:

Francis was but twenty years old. How noble he must have thought it to answer the call to arms, to follow the red and blue colours of Assisi, to ride to battle with courage and a high heart. But to what humiliation and darkness it led him.

He accompanied the archers and cavalry and took his place with others on the *collestrada* at the bend of the Tiber where the Perugians set upon the Assisians. Poor Francis! He witnessed the slaughter and bloodshed, was exposed to the cruelty and hatred of the larger Perugian force, and providentially was taken prisoner. There, at Ponte San Giovanni was much blood shed, and there blessed Francis was first exposed to the inhumanity of men at war.

There followed Vanna's meditation on the bridge of St John, built to reconcile the two banks of the Tiber but that day made to be the place of bloodshed and enmity. Jacopone read on about the early cheerfulness of Francis' captivity in the face of teasing and taunting by some of the older and awkward men, and then he detected a change of tone:

Francis of sensitive soul, lover of nature and son of the open country of Umbria, you began to feel the oppressive weight of incarceration and yearned for the heights of Mount Subasio and the wide skies above Assisi. Darkness and melancholy fell upon your sunny soul and some strange suffocating fever took hold on you.

Jacopone turned the parchment and remembered the story of the alarming change which had taken place in Francis when he returned to Assisi. First of all he was welcomed following his release, and the young men of the town elected him "king of revels" for a night and began a spree of gluttony and drunkenness which revolted Francis' soul. He followed them far behind, holding his revel's staff in his hand as he felt again death's sickness upon him. Soon he took to his bed, and Vanna recorded the emptiness of soul which made him aware of his spiritual poverty. She copied out the words of Thomas of Celano:

When Francis recovered enough to leave his bed, with the aid of a stick, he went "to look curiously on the landscape around . . . at the beauty of the fields, the pleasantness of the vineyards, on anything that is fair to see." But the prison had done its work, and how marvellously our Lord caused Francis to lose all sense of beauty in the world around, and all proud and arrogant hopes of his own making. All savour in living was gone, and the delirious singing of the troubadour songs, with the allurements of the world of colour and sense, had given way to some strange melancholy of soul. In such a way did the love of God prepare in Francis' heart a place for the wounding and the glory of Christ.

How did Vanna understand the emptiness of Francis' soul when she was so young and fair? wondered Jacopone. His knees were aching and he rose and sat upon the bed with the manuscript in his lap. "These words comfort me in my sadness," he murmured. "Was it destined that I should find this manuscript?"

He went on to read of the sudden euphoric mood which followed so quickly upon Francis' melancholy, caused by the summons from the young Count Gentile to leave his father's house and serve as a knight under the legendary hero Walter de Brienne. Three years after the imprisonment at Perugia Francis made another attempt at worldly honours. "Poor Francesco," wrote Vanna, "the first stage of this new journey measured five hundred kilometres — but you only covered fifty."

In Spoleto Francis felt the sickness again and dreamed of the hall of a glorious lord, its walls covered with tapestries, shields and banners of colour and splendour. "Whom would you serve," asked a voice in the dream, "the master or the servant?" Francis answered that he would, of course, serve the master. "Why then do you run away from the master who is God," came the voice again, "and follow the mere servant? Return to Assisi and you will discover where your future lies."

Vanna recorded the following months of perplexity and trial while Francis in anguish of spirit considered what he should do. She followed his wanderings around the caves and rocks of Mount Subasio and his prayers and vigils in the half-abandoned chapels which were dotted around the hillsides surrounding Assisi.

Jacopone remembered one of these — the one to which Vanna had taken him one day when they went on an excursion to the slopes of Mount Subasio. During the afternoon she had said: "Jacopo, do you want to please me?"

"I always want to please you," he replied.

"I would very much like to visit the church of San Damiano where the crucified Christ spoke to Francis."

It was not that Jacopone was opposed to religion. He simply had no time for it in his busy life. Indifference was his sin — together with an abhorrence of the emotional and somewhat sadistic religion displayed by the flagellants who had wandered around parts of central Italy some years before.

But on that day, pressed by Vanna, he accompanied her towards the church of San Damiano which, since the day of Francis' vision, had been repaired first of all by Francis himself with his friends, and later had become the convent for St Clare and those who shared with her in the life of prayer.

They wandered down the hill on that beautiful afternoon, trailing through the long grasses and wild red poppies which covered the hillside and bordered the rough path towards the convent. The braying of a donkey in the distance mingled with birdsong as Vanna took Jacopone's hand, and the heady smell of late summer surrounded them as they approached the solitary olive tree which stood guardian at the door of the barn-like church. A line of cypresses stood behind San Damiano and the blue and pink Appennines rose in the distant west.

Jacopone's life had been too worldly, too busy, too professional and fastidious to make time for the kind of religion that surrounded him in Todi and the province of Umbria. He was not interested in the scholastic dogma he had met at Bologna in his student days and was cynical about the establishment religion of the nobility and merchant classes. He viewed with caution and disdain the emotional excesses of the extreme penitents with their blend of asceticism and hysterical joy.

But on this day with Vanna something happened. At the door of the church Jacopone hesitated. Momentarily he caught his breath and broke out in a flushing of the face and perspiration upon his brow.

"What's the matter Jacopo?" asked Vanna anxiously. "Are you not well?"

"It's all right Vanna," Jacopone answered rather too quickly. "It must be the heat of the day — I feel that I must not. . . . Oh, never mind, lets go in and have done with it."

Vanna wondered at this sudden turn about of attitude but she said no more and led him into the tiny church, asking permission of one of the sisters of St Clare to pray before the Byzantine crucifix which, in the spring of 1206, had spoken to Francis, calling him to follow the crucified Christ.

There was no-one else in the church or sanctuary, and the sunlight streamed through one of the windows, lighting the face of Christ whose hands and feet were transfixed to His cross, though there was a regal bearing in His body and an expression of patience and love upon His face.

Vanna knelt and Jacopone sat beside her. She soon became lost in prayer and meditation and Jacopone looked fully upon the crucifix. Suddenly there came over him again that feeling of faintness, accompanied this time by breathlessness and a strange tingling in his hands and feet.

He was frightened, and though he tried to hide it from Vanna he felt himself trembling all over and could hardly get his breath. "Vanna, Vanna,' he whispered hoarsely, then left her kneeling while he stumbled out into the open air to sit on the low wall at the front of the church near the olive tree, gasping for breath and confused in his mind. The Clare sister watched him quietly and carefully from the door but did not intervene.

All this had happened a year ago just before their marriage, and Jacopone had succeeded in putting it out of his mind, though Vanna had pondered it silently in her own heart.

Seated upon his bed with Vanna's manuscript on his knee Jacopone allowed himself to be exposed to the experience again, feeling that strange tingling in hands and feet as he fixed his mind's eye upon the crucifix, feeling it call to him from the town of Assisi and from deep within his own heart.

But what had Vanna written of Francis' encounter with the crucified Christ? He looked at the manuscript again and suddenly his heart leaped. He read his own name in the narrative and realized that she had penned the words immediately after that remembered visit. The clear, round handwriting spelled out a message from the other side of death:

San Damiano! It was my second visit today and what feelings were stirred up within me. And for my dear Jacopo too! I was not at first aware of how much it affected him, for my intense desire to return there was because my first visit so moved me and drew me to the crucified Saviour that Francis loved.

My great desire was to feel again the joy and sadness of that crucifix, so when Jacopo stood faint and hesitant at the door I thought it to be no more than the heat of the day. As I knelt in prayer I almost lost myself in meditation on the wounds and compassion of Christ.

Suddenly Jacopo began spluttering and trembling, and he stumbled out out of the church. Following after him I found him taking great gasps of air and speechless with bewilderment and confusion.

Part of me was anxious lest he was really ill, but part of me began to sing for joy, for Jacopo — my dear Jacopo — was deeply moved by the risen Lord Jesus, the great King of Heaven.

Dear Jesus, by your wounded hands and feet, by your pierced heart of love, draw Jacopo to yourself — that we may be united in our love for you . . .

There was no more manuscript. Had Vanna continued her meditations elsewhere or had she written nothing from the time they were married? Or, thought Jacopone, was this all he needed at this time? He quickly looked through the rest of Vanna's belongings but there did not appear to be any more of her writing. Perhaps this was sufficient. Jacopone knew that his salvation had to do with the crucified Jesus and with the story of Francis.

His mind was in a turmoil. The foundation upon which his former life had been built was breaking up under the onslaught of bereavement, loneliness and the revelation of an entirely new, spiritual, dimension of life.

It was not that he had rejected the faith upon which Vanna had built her life, but that he had thought himself exempt from such claims. His life, worldly and aloof, had had no place for the suffering Jesus. They had nothing in common. But now?

He found it difficult to think clearly. His former reasoning now seemed false, his values proved empty and vain. He thought of the pattern of Jesus, of Francis, of Vanna. In each case there was compassion and love, and in each case there was penance, suffering and death. But also in each case he felt himself presented with a word of revelation and a question that demanded from him an answer. The question had to do with the direction of his life from this moment. The answer was not in the solution of a rational or legal problem. He could have come to terms with that. It was the answer of love in response to Love — and he hardly knew how to formulate the question let alone frame the answer.

There were two things he must do. First he must seek help from the convent of San Fortunato in Todi. The friars would tell him the full story of St Francis and give him instruction from the Gospels. Then he must return to San Damiano and gaze upon that crucifix which had spoken to Francis and had stirred Vanna's heart to love, and which had perplexed and afflicted him when she had taken him there. He had understood nothing before Vanna's death, but now the way was becoming clear!

Then, as if all this mental turmoil on top of his bereavement and lethargy was too much for him, he lay on his low bed, surrounded by Vanna's papers and belongings, and went to sleep.

The weeks that followed were a puzzle to the people of Todi. At first there had been great sympathy for Jacopone. Everyone was moved by the way in which the arrogant notary, the stiff and fastidious professional man, had been smitten by the sudden

27

tragedy of Vanna's death. They realized how deeply he had loved her and were ready to bear some of the sorrow, generous in understanding his erratic behaviour and crazed state of mind.

But when this state of affairs did not lessen but also took a religious and manic turn their curiosity turned to antagonism. Jacopone's behaviour became absurd and his "turn about" attitude became unacceptable.

There was, for instance, the matter of poverty. Some weeks after Vanna's death Jacapone sold his property and distributed the proceeds among the poor. The rational Doctor of Law, the comfort-loving connoisseur of good food and delicate living, suddenly displayed a mania for poverty, and first privately, and then publicly, gave away almost all that he owned.

At first this caused great joy and wonder among the common people. But as he stripped his house and himself of goods and possessions, people began to feel uncomfortable and many of those who had at first thanked him for his generosity became sullen.

Then, roughly dressed and unkempt, he set off one morning to the convent of San Fortunato in Todi to ask the Franciscan friars to receive him as a penitent and novice. This was a friary of the *mitigati* or relaxed rule, despised by the *zelanti* who held to the original and primitive vision of St Francis.

The convent was set back from the road, with an outer gate in the surrounding wall and a large garden before the main building. He got no further than the inside of the first walled gate. Some of the more relaxed brothers were gossiping together in the garden and Brother Alberto the Guardian was not among them. The porter-brother stood in his way, for Jacopone's reputation for madness had gathered momentum in the previous weeks.

"Whoa, hold on there Jacopone!" he cried. "You're behaving like a donkey — you have no place in this herd. What do you want?"

"I want, my brother, to be recognized as a fool and to share the life of our father Francis with you. Will you take me in?"

Brother Sebastiano, the friary wag, looked scornfully on the scraggy, ragged and no longer youthful Jacopone and cried out: "You have changed your tune, Master Jacopone. There was a time when you laughed at us poor donkeys. Well, if you wish to live with us you must become a donkey too — that as a donkey you may dwell among donkeys."

Jacopone stood still, stared dumbly at Sebastiano, then turned and ran out of the gate and down the road. "It seems that was not to his taste," smirked one of the others. "Perhaps his dramatic conversion does not reach that far."

Within half an hour Jacopone was back. He had stripped to the waist, was wrapped around with an ass's skin and lumbered up the steps into the garden on all fours, almost braying: "Brothers, here I am, become a donkey. Admit the donkey, then, to live among the donkeys."

The literal interpretation was too much for the *mitigati* friars. Some of them simply laughed while two of the stouter ones took up Jacopone and dumped him unceremoniously outside the gate into the road — ass's skin and all. Then they locked the outside gate.

"He is more fit for the *zelanti* friars," said Sebastiano. "Let him bray to them. I don't think we need tell brother Alberto of this episode."

Jacopone got to his feet, accepting such degradation as simply as he felt Francis would have done. He was not a man of hidden devotion. He had once loved and coveted the world and now he despised it. So he wandered through the streets of Todi in his ass's skin, arousing contempt, merriment, laughter and pity by turn. He was pelted with stones by the children who shouted, *"Pazzo, pazzo!"*

Some of his former friends, believing his grief was to blame, tried to remonstrate with him and lead him away from the public eye. But the more they tried to quieten him the more vociferous he became in his protests. There was an element of enjoyment in his exhibitionism as well as of genuine penitence and disdain of the world. And any sense of prophetic symbolism was lost on them!

One who did begin to understand was his former friend Valerio. After patiently listening to one of Jacopone's calls for repentance outside the Todi market one day, Valerio asked him to carry a pair of chickens home while he paid some calls in the town. Jacopone took the chickens and carried them "home" to Valerio's family vault in the parish church. Valerio grasped the message and appreciated it. But the story went the rounds and the people laughed and pitied.

A week or so later Brother Alberto returned to Todi and Jacopone decided to make a proper entrance to San Fortunato, though he did nothing about his rough and unkempt appearance. He chose the time when he knew the friars would be gathered in chapter. The outside gate was unlocked so he went up the steps, through the garden and began knocking loudly at the main door.

Before the porter-brother could protest or hold him back Jacopone brushed past him and burst in upon the friars. "My brothers," he cried — and some of them noted the wild gleam in his eye, "my sins and follies have caught up with me and I want to throw in my lot with you in penitence and faith. Take me in, I pray, and teach me penance, that my life may be made acceptable to God."

This caused great confusion among the friars. Some members of the chapter, including Sebastiano, withdrew and would have nothing to do with the mad religious fool that Jacopone had become; they would not even discuss the matter. Others, believing that he had become deranged and that his religious conversion was a lie, argued that there was certainly no place for him among the Conventual friars.

But some — including Brother Alberto — had the gift of discernment and realized that Jacopone needed comfort and counsel in the context of retreat and tranquillity.

Rising from his seat below the crucifix in the chapter room the Guardian went over to Jacopone, putting his hand on his arm. "Come Jacopone,' he murmured, "and we will talk together." He led him down the corridor and Jacopone followed in silence as the other friars stood back and made way for them both. So while the community was left divided into at least three factions, Alberto, a wise spiritual physician began to lead Jacopone into an understanding of the state of his soul.

"Now first of all, Jacopone, tell me what is going on in that head of yours, and why you are trying to take the kingdom of heaven by force, throwing the whole of Todi into confusion and losing the sympathy and understanding of the townsfolk. Tell me plainly, take your time — my ears are open."

Jacopone sat in the rays of the sun beside the window in the Guardian's room. He looked gaunt, weary, unkempt and ragged. As he talked, Alberto noted signs of madness as he dribbled into his matted beard, and he listened to the confused turbulence of words as Jacopone spilled out the empty bankruptcy of his soul in the light of bereavement and what he had discovered.

Alberto heard words of genuine distress, profound penitence and the beginnings of true faith. Jacopone's penitence was leading him into a desire for harsh penance and strict asceticism. He clearly wanted to atone for his past, to deal cruelly with his soft body, to have vengeance on his former luxury. He wanted to identify with the crucified Jesus.

After the first flood of penitence had abated he sat still breathing heavily and then went on in a quieter tone. "I remember that day with Vanna at San Damiano. She knew how hard my heart was, and that Christ sought to call me into His way then. But I was too stubborn, for as soon as I saw that look of tenderness in the eyes of the Saviour I turned away and stumbled out of the church. And I resisted Him until my pride was laid low and the death of my beloved Vanna exposed the emptiness of my soul."

Brother Alberto laid his hand on Jacopone's shoulder. "Ah yes," he said quietly. "You have been brought through the dark valley of bereavement and sorrow and you have allowed the good Spirit of God to lead you to penitence. But, Jacopone, you must not be too harsh with yourself. Do you not see that the way of Jesus is the way of love? First of all you must receive forgiveness and allow patience and compassion to have their way in your soul. However deep your grief for past sin, *you* can never atone, for you are the sinner. This is the reason why we look to the Saviour Christ. You are indulging in the heresies of which the flagellants are guilty. We are not saved by beating ourselves into submission for it is Christ's shed blood, and not ours, that cleanses from sin."

Jacopone stood up suddenly, his eyes flashing. "But you do not understand, father," he cried. "The flagellants are right and I did not see it. They see how filthy human sin is. They show their repentance publicly and gladly make themselves fools for God's sake. That is what I need, for I have been arrogant and proud and need to be brought low."

"I think you have been brought low enough," replied Alberto. "Come now and make your confession to our heavenly Father. I will give you a work of penance and you will receive the healing of God's absolution. Then go back into the world and pick up the threads of your life again.

"I do not think that God calls you at this time to the religious life. You are too hasty in your judgement. Time will heal your wounds a little and give you back something of your former wisdom without its arrogance and folly. The ways of God are gentle, and you, of all people, need such gentleness now. I think Vanna would agree with me."

At the mention of her name Jacopone became quiet again. After some gentle persuasion he allowed himself to be led to the convent chapel. He made his confession, heard Alberto's clear words of absolution and then was told that his penance was to take up his pen and write poetry again — but this time of the love and mercy of God.

Brother Alberto knew that the divine Love could not immediately fill Jacopone's heart, but the process of transformation had begun, and the grace of God was already at work. Alberto also knew that the alternation between deep penitence and burning faith would continue to perplex the new-born soul. A period of residence in the convent and instruction in the Gospel would be beneficial just at this point, but Alberto was also aware that the present temper of the *mitigati* brothers would not allow this to happen. Apart from the problems presented by what some of them called Jacopone's madness there was also the thorny question of poverty — one which divided the Franciscan Order itself.

These are difficult days for the Order," sighed Alberto. "There are many good souls among the Conventuals and among the Spirituals, but they often work against each other and bring sadness to our Saviour's heart."

He knew how Francis must have felt and then wondered if he was in the right place himself, as the Guardian of a house under the mitigated rule. The problem was not made easier by the fiery Italian temperament, and he smiled to himself as he thought of his German grandmother and of the influence she had had on his family and upbringing.

Before Jacopone went on his way Brother Alberto took him to the kitchen where they ate some Umbrian pastries and drank some of the local wine together. "Listen, Jacopone," said Alberto smiling, "I am not making a final decision about you becoming a novice. Vocations need time to develop, and discernment is needed. I am saying that you require time for reflection, for growth in your new life, for spiritual roots to go down deep into the soil. Only after such a time of waiting, testing and experience will you realize what it means for your will to be given completely to God. Then you will return . . . and we shall see."

Jacopone sat still without speaking. then he looked into Alberto's eyes, sighed and nodded his head.

Alberto reached down into the folds of his grey habit: "I recommend you to take this book of the Gospels, make another pilgrimage to San Damiano and trace the story of Francis around Assisi and over Mount Subasio. It is a long way from the

San Damiano crucifix to the deep darkness and glory of Mount La Verna, and such a journey may take many years of travelling. Your pilgrimage is to be an interior one, but first of all plant your feet upon the solid ground of Umbria and take slow and firm steps. God will lead, and I will remain your friend."

Brother Alberto was not given to emotional excess but he impulsively took Jacopone in his arms and Jacopone laid his head on the Guardian's shoulder. They shed some tears together and remained in this embrace for nearly a minute.

Jacopone felt a deep sense of peace as well as a powerful spirit of urgency communicated in Alberto's words. The peace was a result of the absolution, and the urgency was the awareness that he had received his mission, though he knew only the first few steps of the journey.

He knelt at Brother Alberto's feet, received his blessing and resolutely made his way back into the town. "I will set out as soon as I can to walk to Assisi," he thought. "I will begin my pilgrimage from this place, and whether by wisdom or folly I will follow Christ as Francis did. And may God help me."

4   Ascetic Pilgrim

When Jacopone had visited Assisi and San Damiano with Vanna before their marriage they had travelled from Todi by donkey carriage. Now Jacopone set out alone on foot. It was a journey of memories and penitence. He had with him a knapsack containing a crust of bread, a flask of cheap wine and the book of the Gospels loaned him by Brother Alberto.

Since his rejection as a novice by the friars at San Fortunato he had become more aware of a distinct and older group of friars with a looser organization than the Conventuals or *mitigati*. These were the Spirituals or *zelanti*, and they seemed much more in line with Jacopone's understanding of the poverty and simplicity of St Francis.

Jacopone did not want to lose his friendship with Brother Alberto, but his distaste for the mitigated rule of the Conventional friars had increased — especially since his talks with some of the *zelanti* friars he had met in his wanderings.

The story of Francis was a romantic one, appealing to Jacopone's sense of adventure and radicalism and he knew that the pilgrimage to Assisi would clarify his confused thinking and point him in the right direction.

After the good advice given him by Brother Alberto following his confession and absolution he returned to his now poor and stripped house in Todi. He slept soundly that night and instead of setting off immediately the next day found that he wanted to wait before making the journey, to prepare himself with prayer, inner quietness and a study of the Gospels.

Thus some weeks passed, and he felt the sometimes extreme alternations that Alberto knew would affect his soul. There were still times of distraught perplexity and darkness — and some of his nights were spent in tears and loneliness, often waking suddenly and reaching out for Vanna, only to find the stabbing realization that he would never again touch her on earth.

But there were also times of radiance and joy. Both of these he found in the Franciscan tradition and in the Gospels, for the lives of Francis and of Jesus were filled with joy and sorrow.

Jacopone thought much of the counsel of Brother Alberto in advising him away from a harsh penitence and towards hope, joy and assurance. But he also felt the need for an asceticism through which he could discipline body and mind. He wondered if the mercy and grace which the *mitigati* friars were so fond of extolling really evaded the bitterness and pain of the cross.

He remembered a market-place sermon preached by one of the *zelanti* friars a week or two before, on a text from St Paul: "I buffet my body and bring it into subjection, lest after having preached to others I myself should be disqualified." But then he thought of the words of Brother Alberto, that costly grace was the gift of Christ, and that it was the Saviour's precious blood which alone could wash away the stains of sin, and not the blood of flagellation and asceticism.

With such thoughts he made his way to Assisi, retracing the path that he and Vanna had covered the previous year until he came to the spot where she had asked him to take her to the church of San Damiano.

From there it was only a few kilometres down, past the town of Assisi where some people saw him stumbling and praying, watching him as he made his descent along the path which led to the church and convent of the Clare sisters — the church of San Damiano where they now lived their simple life of prayer and poverty.

He did not now feel that constriction in throat and chest which had afflicted him previously, but he did feel his pulse quicken, his heartbeat sound in his ears, and he became aware of the perspiration upon his forehead and the palms of his hands.

He quietly entered the chapel where the large Byzantine crucifix hung, and found the place where Vanna had knelt. He looked at the gentle and outstretched form of the Christ, not now in agony but with arms extended in invitation and compassion. Here Francis had heard Christ speak to him; here Vanna had been bathed in the love of the crucified One; here Jacopone had been seized with fear and trembling and had fled from the chapel.

But now he knelt in fervent longing, feeling only that strange tingling in hands and feet, and now a burning within his breast which he understood to be the kindling of the fire of divine Love.

He knelt there, losing all sense of time and place, until at last he became conscious of the poor Clare sister kneeling a little space away but beside him. He turned his face towards her and she opened her eyes and smiled. "Are you Ser Jacopone Benedetti?" she asked quietly, "and did you not come here with Vanna di Guidone on that beautiful day a year ago? You have travelled a dark and lonely road since that time."

Jacopone was abashed. His defences fell and he began to cry. He had not sought this, but here was a gentle woman's touch, an understanding heart and the discernment which came from a deep life of prayer.

They began to talk quietly together under the gaze of the loving Christ. The sister told Jacopone that Vanna had sought her advice on her first visit to San Damiano and that they had exchanged a few words when Jacopone had stumbled out of the chapel on her second visit. She had also heard of Vanna's tragic death and had prayed for both Vanna and Jacopone since that time.

When she heard of his rejection by the San Fortunato convent and Brother Alberto's words about vocation, she asked Jacopone if he had thought of joining St Francis' tertiary Order of Penance. This seemed to Jacopone like the very word of God to him, and by the time he was ready to leave San Damiano he had resolved to join the Third Order. He already observed the rule of poverty, penitence and continence.

Feeling happier and consoled by the feminine gentleness and maternal tenderness of the anonymous sister, he made his way back to Todi, donned the rough *bizocone* tunic of the more fervent tertiaries, and sought by reading, prayer and sacrament to nourish his sense of vocation and live a life close to Jesus and Francis.

His days of foolish madness were not over, and never would be to the end of his life. There were many who judged him insane because of his crazy and symbolic actions, but there were others who began to see, to hear and to feel the prophetic power of his singing, praying and preaching in the public places in and around the town of Todi and the whole province of Umbria.

Good and dramatic preaching was scarce enough, for so many churches seemed to have illiterate or indifferent priests. When Jacopone preached from the Old Testament people trembled; when he told the parables of Jesus they were spellbound; when he described Jesus' healing miracles they cried aloud. Repentance, faith and a disciplined following of Christ was his message. He composed Gospel words to common folk tunes and as he set people's feet tapping so he set their hearts yearning for forgiveness, healing and peace.

The eloquence of the former advocate had now given place to the preaching of the cross by a poor mendicant preacher. But he did not always endear himself to his hearers.

One day he went to a marriage feast in his brother's house, tarred and feathered as a rebuke to the worldly glitter and tinsel of the celebration — it was a judgement upon the overloaded tables and flowing wine while the poor eked out their miserable existence in another quarter of the town.

Frederick his brother and the chief guests were furious. "What do you think you are doing, you stupid fool?" whispered his brother loud enough for only Jacopone to hear. "Get out of that crazy costume or get out of this house. I've had enough of your erratic behaviour."

Jacopone stood still and stared at Frederick. Then he turned to the people looking on, and said: "As my brother intends to honour the family by his wealth and intelligence, so I wish to honour it by my imbecility." Some saw this as yet another example of lunacy, and others as the strain of holy madness which increasingly characterized the *zelanti* tradition of the Franciscan life.

As he read, prayed, preached and sang, so he wrote poems and popular hymns, fulfilling Alberto's counsel and finding joy in making songs for penitents to sing. His mood swung between penitence and joy, but he found great delight in using Umbrian folk melodies and troubadour love tunes to convey spiritual fervour and enthusiasm.

He continued to live in poverty and simplicity until one evening he felt he had given in to the temptation to compromise his new life. An old friend invited him to dine with him in his home, and they reminisced together over the meal and the wine.

When Jacopone left the house late that night the cold air brought him to his senses. Guilt and fear took hold of him. He ran and stumbled back to his ascetic dwelling and in a spirit of penitence wrote a poem under the title: *Of Watchfulness Over the Senses:*

> *Friend, beware lest you fall:*
> > *Beware!*

First, beware your spiritual foe,
Who in friend's disguise would go,
Trust him not, he brings you woe:
> *Beware!*

Turn your *eyes* away from ill,
Evil sights may wound your will;
Healing then takes longer still:
> *Beware!*

Evil tongues a snare will set;
Stop your *ears* — still closer yet!
Lest they catch you in their net:
              Beware!

Put a bridle on your *taste:*
Gluttony turns to poisonous waste,
Lust then follows on in haste:
              Beware!

Smells and savours perilous,
Fragrances insidious —
May God keep them far from us:
              Beware!

God is shamed by sinful *touch*
Set your guard and keep your watch!
Lest you perish in its clutch:
              Beware!

Godless relations set apart,
Lest they turn your steadfast heart,
And they cause you wound and smart:
              Beware!

So-called friends will throng around,
Run like ants, like ants abound,
Dry your roots in God's good ground:
              Beware!

And beware lest evil thought
Wound and drag your mind to naught;
Sicken all your soul distraught:
              Beware!

Then there were times when the Spirit of the Lord caught up Jacopone in prayer and he forgot all his harsh asceticism in the delights of love. He could not bear the sweet honey of sentimentalism and was certainly no born optimist, but when he was caught up in the fervour of joy he abandoned himself to it. So discipline and spontaneity became evident as the two poles of his religious experience.

He knew that St Francis had been described as "drunken with the love and compassion of Christ", breaking out in wild troubadour rejoicings in honour of Christ his love. So Jacopone began to experience periods of rapturous adoration in which he had no power over himself but burst into incoherent songs and cries.

He called such emotional exaltation *Jubilus*, thinking of it as the fire of the divine Love burning within the human soul. The recipient had little control over it, but rather desired to submit himself to the divine Spirit who stirred up the heart to fervent love and song.

One early evening he went to meditate in the fields which bordered the town of Todi, surrounded by the beauty of the Umbrian landscape. After a period of reflection upon the Gospel he sank down into silent meditation beneath the shade of a leafy tree.

Suddenly he seemed surrounded by music. His heart began that strange burning and he felt himself inebriated by the love of Christ. He got to his feet and began to dance, and he danced over the fields, up into the town, threading his way through the small groups of people nodding and gossiping in the evening sun.

"Go to it, Jacopone," laughed one group of workmen sitting outside a tavern. There were smiles and laughter as they chattered together about the antics which Jacopone had got up to since his life had taken such a dramatic turn. There was no derisive shouting of *"Pazzo! Pazzo!"* now, for even among those who reacted with pity or glee at such a spectacle there was an awareness that some profound transformation was taking place in Jacopone's life.

This was no manifestation of craziness, and certainly not dark madness, but a spirit of lightness and song that shed fragrance, melody and radiance about him. He danced home that night, and when he got some control over his head and fingers he wrote: *Of the Jubilus of the Heart, that Breaks Forth in the Voice:*

> *O Jubilus, my heart you move,*
> *And make me sing for very love.*

The *Jubilus* in fire awakes
  And straight the man must sing and pray;
His tongue in childish stammering shakes,
  He knows not what his lips may say,
  He cannot quench or hide away
    That Sweetness pure and infinite.

The *Jubilus* in flame is lit,
  And straight the man must shout and sing;
So close to Love his heart is knit,
  He scarce can bear the burning sting;
  His clamour and his cries must ring,
    And shame for ever take to flight.

The *Jubilus* enslaves man's heart,
  — A love-bewildered prisoner —
And see! his neighbours stand apart,
  And mock the senseless chatterer;
  They think his speech a foolish blur,
    A shadow on his spirit's light.

Yes! when you enter soul and mind,
  O *Jubilus,* you rapture fair,
The heart of man new skill will find
  Love's own disguise to grasp and wear,
  The suffering of Love to bear
    With song and clamour of delight.

And so the uninitiate
  Will think that you are crazed indeed;
They see your strange and fevered state
  But have not wit your heart to read;
  Within, deep-pierced, that heart may bleed,
    Hidden from curious mortal sight.

When Jacopone had finished the lines he lay still and thought about them. It was now as if he were lying at the edge of a vast ocean of glory and love, with the gentle waves breaking in upon him and rushing back again to the bosom of the great ocean. He was embraced and desolate — wounded and burning for love. How could he be so satisfied — and yet so lonely? How could the bright shining of Love's illumination break his heart with both sorrow and joy? He felt himself to be not only upon the shore of the divine Love, but also a part of the divine mystery.

He remembered Brother Alberto's words, that he was on a pilgrimage from the crucifix of San Damiano to the sacred mountain of La Verna. He had never been to La Verna where Francis had entered into the love and sorrow of Calvary and had received in his body the stigmata — wounds of Christ in hands and feet and side. Jacopone shuddered and lay for a time upon the ground, feeling himself drawn in that same direction. It was about eighteen months before Jacopone's mind became clearer. He realized that the effect of Vanna's death was not only a distraught madness mixed with the deep loneliness that had tempted him to suicide, but also a profound sense of being acted upon — even moved from within.

He had not anticipated the grim tragedy of the severing of Vanna's young life. Neither had he expected the first powerful thrust of conversion which had smitten him and sprung up within him as an immediate result of his bereavement. The strange thing was that this conversion seemed dependent upon his bereavement, and the depth and thrust of his conversion drew its power and intensity from his grief.

How different was the pattern of his life from that of St Francis! Though enamoured of Lady Poverty, Francis had not been smitten and wounded by romantic love. As a young man he had quickly become disillusioned with worldly wealth and military honours, had known imprisonment, sickness, and looked into the face of decaying mortality in being exposed to the corrupt and stinking body of the leper — a living death. All this had led to repentance and faith, and when he saw and heard the crucified Christ inviting, calling, commanding, he summoned all the dynamic and enthusiasm of youth to answer the call.

Jacopone's path was different. And yet he felt the same disillusion, the same thrilling call. He looked to Francis now as father and saintly guide in the spiritual life — though his saintliness far exceeded anything Jacopone could hope to attain or understand. He thought again of Brother Alberto's words about his pilgrimage which implied that it would include a journey to La Verna. For Jacopone that name was enshrouded in mystery. Mingling with these thoughts was the realization that an amazing and mysterious transformation was taking place in his own soul.

The emotional energy of almost forty years had been poured into his love for Vanna. Her loss had shaken his physical and emotional life to its foundations and brought him to the edge of madness. Sometimes he suspected that much of his love had been dominated by a grasping *eros* that gloried in desire, pride and arrogance. Even his love for Vanna had been corrupted by carnal avarice. He had gloried in her physical beauty but when she would have spoken to him of Christ he had silenced her.

She had understood this all along. When Jacopone had spoken with the Poor Clare nun at San Damiano he had understood that Vanna had claimed him in love and prayer for the crucified Jesus, though she had not realized that the cost would be her own life. It was as if her spirit was near one evening as he sat in his now poor house in Todi. "Ah, my dear Vanna," murmured Jacopone, "why did I not listen to you? Why did I not realise my own bankruptcy? Why did I silence you when you tried to lead me in the way of Christ's love?"

Only now did he begin to see that he had to be brought to the verge of madness before his arrogance could be toppled and his pride vanquished. So narrow and bigoted had been his heart that there had been no room for God, and only such a crisis as Vanna's death and his own madness could have shaken the foundations of his complacency.

"I feel like the prodigal Son in our Saviour's parable," he sighed. "For having come to himself in the pig-sty he turned his face towards his father's house. The joy and rejoicing with which I have been received is the glorious side of my madness. But it is a longer and more exacting journey to the depths of the Father's heart."

So saying he realized that Alberto's advice about pilgrimage embraced a longer and more demanding journey than he had envisaged — perhaps in reality to La Verna. Only in such a pilgrimage of penance and prayer could his spirit find its true orientation. Saul of Tarsus had needed the desert of Arabia after his conversion so that the powers of the new birth could be established in him. So Jacopone needed more time and solitude for prayer, for thought, for a perusal of the Gospels and of the life of the blessed Francis.

In this frame of mind he set off next morning to see Brother Alberto again. Not this time to seek admission to San Fortunato but for advice to prepare himself for the work of prayer and mission that opened up before him.

The porter-friar was wary of Jacopone when he opened the door to his knocking, eyeing him as he stood still and courteous on the threshold. "You had better come in," he said grudgingly, "but wait there in the vestibule until I see if the Guardian will receive you."

Jacopone was no sooner announced than Alberto came out to meet him. "Come in, Jacopo," he cried. "You are looking more like your old self!" Then he stopped and smiled. "Oh no, Jacopo, that is far from the truth. I should say that you are looking more like your new self — that is nearer the mark!"

"I am weary of my old self," murmured Jacopone as Alberto led him to his own cell. "I feel that I must make a journey to distance myself from what used to be, and to enter into what must be. And I need your counsel."

They sat together, and although Alberto was deeply aware of the desire for pilgrimage and the restlessness that disturbed

Jacopone, he also felt the new sense of sanity and equilibrium that possessed him.

"So you are following the counsel I gave you some months back," said Alberto encouragingly, "and you are attending mass regularly. I was hearing confessions at San Damiano lately and learned that you had received some wise counsel from one of the sisters there. It seems as if the good Lord is ministering to you just as you need Him."

"Yes father," replied Jacopone, "but I have a problem. My mind is clearing and I realize that what you prescribed is what I really need — a time here in this friary under your instruction so that my will may be subdued and a strong discipline applied to my body and soul. I have lived so long in pride and sin that discipline and asceticism come hard to me. And I have been wondering about the spiritual pilgrimage from San Damiano to La Verna."

"You remember that I told you not to be too hard with yourself," replied Alberto gently. He laid his hand upon a copy of the scriptures that lay open upon the table under the window. "This book is the pattern for our life, as our father Francis wished it to be. The spiritual athlete does not indulge in an excess of discipline. You must read Holy Scripture with the Church and not exercise private judgement. It seems to me that you admire John the Baptist more than our Lord Jesus!"

"But did not our father Francis treat his body harshly?" countered Jacopone. "Did not the apostle Paul say: 'I buffet my body and subdue it, lest after having preached to others I myself should become a castaway'?"

"I see your pagan education is paying dividends," laughed Alberto. "Yes, you are right and you are wrong. Francis dealt too harshly with his poor body, as he realized too late. It would have been better if he had treated it with love and humour like the poor ass he called it. And St Paul did not wear a hair shirt or flagellate himself. The tribulations which came to him on account of the Gospel were enough to wear out his poor body. Have you forgotten that I told you that at present you need love and gentleness, and that your pilgrimage was to be an interior one? In time that will bring its own asceticism, and the love of Christ within you will then enable you to bear it."

As he said this he suddenly but gently pulled a cord at Jacopone's neck and exposed the rough edge of a hair shirt as Jacopone, too late, tried to flinch away. He laid his hand over Alberto's, restraining him. "My father," he said quietly, looking into Alberto's eyes, "that is not for ascetism, but in memory of Vanna . . ."

Alberto smiled sadly and nodded, taking his hand away. "I understand, Jacopone — and I think you are beginning to understand too. For love's sake — that is the meaning and centre of the faith of Christ. I see that the Holy Spirit has charge of you and you need only confirmation and encouragement from me. Now this is what I think you should do. You cannot remain here with us at present, and the journey to La Verna lies in the future. You can, though, begin a new pilgrimage.

"You know that our father Francis, when the people of Cannara in hasty zeal wanted to enter the religious life, commended to them the Third Order, thus leaving them free to earn their daily bread, to bring up their children and to live the life of Christ in the midst of the world.

"But there was more to it than that — and this is where you may profit, Jacopo. Those tertiaries who were free from family and worldly ties were able to exercise their freedom in pilgrimage to the Holy Land or the shrines of Christendom or to live out a life of prayer in solitary places. Now you have given away your property and are free from worldly ties, so why not set out and visit the Franciscan sites made holy by those who have followed Francis diligently? You should begin at the Portiuncula below Assisi — I believe Brother Rufino is still living there and you may find Brother Leo living in some Umbrian cave and perhaps talk with Brother John of Parma. There may also be some friars in the Marches of Ancona who you would find to your liking."

As Alberto spoke he seemed to be taken out of himself, and Jacopone saw tears in his eyes.

"My father," he replied — and there was a puzzled note in his response, "these men you have mentioned are of the *zelanti* friars, called the Spirituals. And you are Guardian of this Conventual friary with a *mitigati* and relaxed rule. Why do you commend me to *them*? And how is it that you speak of them with charity and even with tears?"

Alberto sighed, took Jacopone's arm and pulled him down on to his knees. "Let us pray," he said, "for things are not always what they seem." So saying he commended Jacopone to God's gracious care, made the sign of the cross upon him and bundled him out through the side door before he could ask any more awkward questions.

After Jacopone had gone Alberto picked up a scrap of parchment from the floor, which had fallen from Jacopone's ragged pocket. It was part of a poem which Jacopone had scribbled, and Alberto smiled as he remembered giving him "the writing of poetry" as part of his penance on that day of first confession two years before. The words ran:

God does not lodge in narrow heart;

Love claims the whole and spurns the part.

Great-hearted one, from this do not depart:

    "You shelter Deity."

Alberto thought of the long and exacting journey into the mystery of the divine Love. "Ah yes," he whispered, "it is a long pilgrimage from San Damiano to La Verna!"

The Portiuncula below Assisi, where the small church of Saint Mary of the Angels stood, was some forty kilometres from Todi. It had belonged to the Benedictine Abbey on Monte Subasio but the monks had left it to decay, causing the fresco of the Assumption to fade and crumble. When Francis had found the already seven-hundred-year-old chapel in the midst of a forest of oaks he was seized with a desire to restore it, so the

48

Benedictine's gave it over to him for a rent of a basket of fish annually.

It was here on St Matthias' Day in 1209, when hearing mass, that Francis was first challenged with the Gospel call from St Matthew: "Go preach, saying the Kingdom of Heaven is at hand; heal the sick, cleanse the lepers; freely ye have received, freely give . . ." And when Francis sought an exposition of the Gospel reading the priest told him that the disciples of Christ had received the commission to preach Gospel penitence everywhere, without carrying anything with them, and to depend on God alone to provide for their needs.

Francis had trembled with happiness at this revelation, and Jacopone felt the same enthusiastic response which had filled Francis' heart when he said: "This is what I wish. This is what I am seeking. This I long with all my inmost heart to do." Jacopone did not remember where he had heard or read it, but he knew that from that moment, overflowing with joy, Francis threw away his staff, cast off his outer garment, keeping only his tunic, and replaced his leather girdle with a cord and made himself a rough habit that no-one would covet! Thus he obeyed literally the call of the Gospel and the words of Jesus, deliberately following and proclaiming the way of Christ.

Francis was said to have loved the Portiuncula more than any other place in the world. As Jacopone drew near to the clearing in the woods the evening sun made a mottled pattern on the path which led to the chapel. He could hardly contain himself as he entered, for the atmosphere was alive with the joy of Francis and yet with a tender sorrow that moved him to the depths of his being. He had always believed that there were holy places associated with great manifestations of God or with the holiness of saints. But this was the first time he had been exposed to such seemingly palpable holiness. There were, of course, his experiences at San Damiano, but they had been somewhat frightening!

Old Brother Rufino was living there and he carried still the fragrance of simple holiness that Francis had recognized, saying that "his was one of the holiest souls that God had in all the world." He met Jacopone and greeted him with few words but with a warm radiance of welcome. Jacopone remembered that Rufino had a stammer which did not allow him to become a popular preacher, but he had developed a deep life of prayer which seemed to engulf Jacopone as he was welcomed to the Portiuncula as a pilgrim.

It was clear that Rufino was not prepared to engage in much conversation at this point, but he suggested that Jacopone should take the Portiuncula donkey up to the hermitage called the Carceri on Mount Subasio above Assisi and spend some days there alone in prayer, returning when Brother Leo was expected back.

Taking the hand of Brother Rufino as he helped him on to the donkey, Jacopone felt himself to be in vital contact with Francis. He rode past the huts of twigs, mud and leafy branches where the friars lived within the simple hedge which served as a wall around the holy place. As the donkey plodded over the paths and through the fields between the Portiuncula and Assisi Jacopone came within sight of the leper-hospital where the early friars worked, then entered the dense oak-wooded forest which bordered the town of Assisi itself.

Skirting the town he led the donkey up the steep climb to the Carceri where he was received quietly but warmly, without fuss and with few words. During the next few days and nights he began to feel the pull and mystery of solitude and high places in his pattern of prayer. He knew that he was a man of the town and the people, but he also felt a profound response to these secret places of hermitage and loneliness where the soul could be exposed to God in sheer nakedness of terror and joy. "Perhaps only souls like Rufino and Leo can bear the full beams of this divine light," thought Jacopone, "and such other fools and lovers of God such as the ecstatic Giles and the holy Bernard who were with Francis in the early days."

Those days and nights at the Carceri gave Jacopone the experience of the sweet embrace of God's tender love, together with periods of deep loneliness and the shedding of tears. He found it hard to explain such tears, for they participated both in joy and sorrow.

He had only to gaze upon the crucifix in the hermitage chapel for tears of grief and pain to reveal the sorrow in his heart. And he had only to look out of the Carceri over the plunging valley below to find that tears welled up spontaneously within him. Mount Subasio was sometimes shrouded in early morning mist, sometimes bright with noonday sunshine and sometimes it stood under the high night sky with stars shining over the immense solitude.

He could sigh and weep, laugh and sing, shout and dance in these solitudes. He felt somehow that he was sharing in the cosmic dance of love and sorrow — pulsing with the heartbeat of the world and sustained by the same Love that moved the moon and stars.

He lost count of the number of days he spent there, but one morning upon waking he felt that the time had come to return to the Portiuncula. The journey took most of the day, for the air of the high Carceri seemed to make him light-headed. He felt that he was in love with God and that he was seeing the whole created world anew.

As he walked and rode he reflected upon the fact that he had not eaten for two days — and then smiled as he thought that Alberto would have told him that this was the true discipline — the asceticism of love. Self-denial was either for the athlete who trained his body for the race or for the lover who cared not for food and drink, for bodily comfort or clothing — because he was in love!

Toward evening he arrived at the Portiuncula and saw before him an old man with white hair and beard who he knew must be Leo — the Leo whom Francis had called *"Frate Pecorella di Dio"*, the Little Sheep of God, because of his sweetness and honesty.

"So you have returned, Jacopone," said Leo. "Rufino thought you would wait until I appeared, and sure enough I have preceded you by but an hour." He smiled a welcome and the strange effect of such humility and gentleness upon Jacopone made him feel weak at the knees and as simple as a child.

"Come!" cried Rufino from one of the huts. "I think you need some of this broth and bread which I have prepared for you both. Too much fasting may produce visions which, though they may not be devilish, are equally not from our Lord!" So chuckling to himself, he welcomed Leo and Jacopone to the simple supper.

After supper Rufino suggested that they join the other few friars who were at the Portiuncula to say Compline together. Then that they should retire for some sleep so that on the morrow, after Leo had celebrated mass, the three should spend an hour in meditation before sharing with Jacopone the stories of the early days with the blessed Francis.

"I believe," said Leo, "that you are a troubadour of God, Jacopone, and on your journey from San Damiano to La Verna you should catch the vision and feel the power of the first love for Jesus which came to us through our father Francis who now beholds His blessed face in glory."

Jacopone trembled with awe at these words and he prayed with the brothers. He suspected that they would spend most of the night in prayer — but on retiring he fell into a deep and quiet sleep, waking only once and feeling, in those moments between waking and sleeping, that palpable sense of presence which saturated the Portiuncula.

5   In Search of Francis

Jacopone was wakened before dawn by the sound of a bell being struck for mass. Hurriedly he dipped his head into the stream near his hut and pulling on his tunic he entered the chapel where there were about a dozen friars lost in prayer.

He had never known a mass celebrated so simply and yet with such an awareness of the presence of God that he thought he was in heaven. Brother Leo stood at the altar, speaking and moving so slowly that in ordinary circumstances the people would have become restless or impatient.

At the words of consecration "*Hoc est enim corpus meum,* This is my body," Brother Leo elevated the host, looked upon it with wonder and replaced it on the paten. He did the same following the words "*Hic est enim calix sanguinis mei,* This is my blood," lifting the chalice and replacing it with awe and trembling.

Jacopone, watching him, saw an old man, weak and shaking, not far from his own death, finding it difficult to genuflect because of his aching joints. And at the same time he saw a haze of glory about his white head and a childlike look of innocence upon his face, with a radiance that put Jacopone in mind of the transfiguration light which surrounded Jesus on Mount Tabor.

He remembered that Francis had gently rebuked Leo for gazing so long into heaven during mass, but in this mingling of wonder and tears Jacopone could have remained all morning.

At last mass was over and Jacopone saw that Leo and Rufino had set aside time for him. They evidently believed that this visit was foreordained and that they had a task before them in communicating the way in which Jesus revealed Himself among the first band of friars which surrounded Francis.

After a light breakfast in one of the huts, Leo suggested that they spend an hour in meditation, asking the Lord to make them responsive in mind and heart and to deliver them from vain and foolish chatter. They found a clearing among the trees some distance from the chapel and Jacopone sat with the two friars as they brought body and mind into stillness.

After a short time Rufino began a barely audible rhythmic prayer which was coupled with his heartbeat and respiration. It was the prayer "*Deus meus et Omnia!* My God and my All!" which Francis had once repeated through the night, secretly observed by Bernard of Quintavalle who had invited Francis into his home in Assisi at the beginning of the adventure.

Following the example of two friars, Jacopone let his body go and felt a light breathing and warmth upon him. It seemed that hardly a quarter of an hour had passed when Leo quietly began to sing: "*Altissimo, omnipotente, bon Signore . . .*"

Most High, omnipotent, good Lord,
To You be ceaseless praise outpoured,
And blessing without measure;
From You alone all creatures came;
No one is worthy You to name . . .

As they sang the sun filtered through the trees giving a dappled appearance to the wood around. Then both Leo and Rufino began to tell Jacopone the stories of the early days with Francis, in the first flush of a new love for Christ. The scintillating stories wove a spell around Jacopone and the restrained enthusiasm of the two holy men fired him with yearning and love for God.

He learned how Rufino, the cousin of St Clare, had spent many hours in prayer and solitude even before he met Francis, and how he stammered with great reticence in the presence of others.

He recounted the day when, because he had been reluctant to go to preach in Assisi, Francis put him under obedience to do so, stripped to the waist. After he had departed Francis relented and quickly followed after him.

He found Rufino in one of the Assisi churches, being laughed at and mocked by the people. In a moment Francis removed his own habit and cried out: "You citizens of Assisi are like the people who crowded around the Christ when He was nailed to His cross. He bore the crown of thorns and with His own tears, sweat and blood surrendered Himself to agony and death for such as you."

"The people were first of all shocked by such an impassioned cry," said Rufino in recounting the story, "but as they saw Francis' own grief and tears the whole congregation were brought to the foot of the cross in repentance and faith."

Then Leo took up the story and spoke of some of the sacred moments of love and prayer with Francis. He did not stammer like Rufino, but he stopped frequently in the rhapsody of story-telling, overcome in reminiscent wonder, as if he were with Francis again in the surrounding countryside of Umbria, wandering around Narni, Fonte Columbo, up to Monte Casale or into Cortona.

At one point Jacopone was so filled with wonder at the events portrayed by Leo that he cried out, "How is it that you remain so humble and gentle?"

Rufino smiled. "Oh, there have been times when the little sheep of God became angry." Then turning to Leo, he said, "Do you remember when Giles told you about the marble collecting box set near the resting-place of our father Francis in the Basilica which Elias was building in Assisi?"

Leo lowered his head and looked at Rufino from beneath knitted brows. "Ah yes," he replied. "I was angry at that arrogant boaster Elias and was determined to smash the marble alms box. Giles warned me that Elias was capable of anything but I didn't care. I possessed more zeal than love in those days and I took a mallet and smashed the box. Elias and his henchman beat me, cursed and imprisoned me — so far had he removed himself from the poverty and simplicity of our father Francis." Then he stopped to get his breath, and added with a mischievous look in his eyes, "I'm ashamed that I acted violently, but I did enjoy doing it — and it was worth the pains!"

At this Jacopone broke in again. "Yes Brother Leo — you and the friars here at the Portiuncula consider the Basilica and the Sacro Convento in Assisi a treason to the ideal of our father Francis. But the Conventual friars acclaim it as the sign of God's blessing as the Order grows in importance and numbers. Is there not a contradiction there? And is there one, or are there two Orders?"

Leo looked narrowly at Jacopone. "Well may you ask! That Elias Bombarone threw off all pretence when our father Francis died. He rode about on horseback, dined luxuriously, with a personal cook and servants, imposed his will, punished recalcitrants without pity, and the rule which was intended to be kept to the letter and *sine glossa* he altered, interpreting and twisting it to his own design.

"I have said many harsh things about him and his extravagances. But he has been dead nearly twenty years — after excommunication and reconciliation. All I can say now is that I wish rest to his soul, in forgiveness and peace."

"But you have not answered my question," persisted Jacopone. "I am anxious to know if the robe of Francis is to remain whole like the garment of Jesus, or is it to be rent into two or three pieces?"

Rufino broke in with a stammer: "There were those, even in our blessed father's lifetime who looked to Elias and his followers, for they wanted a less primitive rule with more comfort and luxury. Now we call them the *relaxi* or *mitigati.* Then there have always been those who sought after learning and pandered to the intellectual life of the Dominicans. We call them the *litterati.* But what has Paris or Bologna to do with Assisi?"

"Yes," responded Jacopone, "and there were those who kept their eyes on the crucified Jesus and followed the life and words of our father Francis. We call them the *zelanti!*"

Leo smiled and enquired, "And with whom do you throw in your lot, Jacopone?" Jacopone looked full into the face of Leo, who caught the smouldering fire of zeal in his eyes. "With the *zelanti!*" he replied without hesitation.

"And what of the garment without rent or schism?" asked Rufino. "Why did you come here some days back to seek us out? Have you not been in touch with the *mitigati* friars in Todi, and have you not asked to be admitted to their convent at San Fortunato?"

The colour drained from Jacopone's face as he looked at them both — two of the last links on the golden chain from Francis himself. He fingered his tertiary tunic nervously. "Yes," he replied. "My heart is with you, but I asked to be received into San Fortunato. There is a Guardian there named Alberto and he showed me quietness and discernment when I was beside myself with grief and madness. He delivered me from the wild excesses of asceticism."

He could not stop there, so he went on to tell them of the many months of madness after the death of Vanna and of the path which had led him to the Portuincula.

Leo listened until he had finished. Then he moved from his place and embraced Jacopone. "Yes, my dear brother," he said gently, "we know of you and your bereavement. We have heard of your trials and the dark night of your soul. We have shared sweet fellowship with Alberto, for there are some precious brothers among the *mitigati* convents in Umbria and throughout Italy. God has his friars minor among the *mitigati* and *litterati* groups. We believe that schism is to be avoided if at all possible, and therefore we strive to keep the garment whole."

Jacopone lifted his head from Leo's shoulder. "My father," he whispered, "Alberto told me I should come to you because you are among those who are called the '*nos qui cum eo fuimus, we who were with him*'."

Rufino smiled at Jacopone's good Latin. "You are right," he responded humorously, "and do you know that you are now in the arms of him who is called '*Leo, qui omnia viderat*'?"

"Leo, who has seen it all," responded Jacopone immediately, and he stood up straight and took the old man Leo by both his shoulders. "Yes my dear fathers, I know it," he said. "And that is why Alberto sent me here. All this leads to one question which I see you have neglected to mention — the question of La Verna. Alberto told me that it was a long journey from San Damiano to La Verna. He meant not a physical journey but a pilgrimage of the heart. Can you enlighten me as to its meaning and tell me what to do?"

Leo began to tremble, and both Rufino and Jacopone took hold of him and sat him down in the shade of the large oak. He was silent for a time and neither of the other two dared break the silence.

Then he looked up through the interlacing branches of the tree as the sun filtered through to where they were seated. Quietly he began to speak. "From San Damiano to La Verna is a long and weary journey. The cross at San Damiano turned night to day for Francis. It shone with a light above the glory of the sun, scattered rays of forgiveness and compassion along the way and brought healing and life to all who looked upon it. So it was for Francis and so it was for all of us."

Then he lowered his eyes, looking at the ground before him. "But the shadow of the cross of La Verna always lay across our path. The crucified One who appeared to Francis turned day to night, devoured our father's heart, burned into his soul and pierced his hands and feet. And yet it is one cross — at San Damiano and La Verna. It opens the eyes of the blind, looses the dumb tongue, plays music into the deaf ear and causes the lame man to dance and sing. It breaks the chains of the prisoner, raises the dead and causes the forgiven sinner to tell all men of the Saviour's love.

"But at La Verna it draws a man into the night of the spirit, deepens the mystery of God, reduces the believer to silence and amazement . . ." Leo began to weep quietly and then reached out and took Jacopone's hand.

"My brother," he said, "it seems that this is your journey — though not yet. You have come to us to receive this word. Both Rufino and I will soon be dead and there will be none left of those who were with him — perhaps then will be your time. We do not desire a rending of the garment of Francis in schism. But we do believe that the vision which the crucified One gave to our blessed father is one which is more important than the preservation of a false unity of organization.

"The Order itself must undergo the purgation of a dark night. And you too, my brother, will have to go this way. There is not just one dark night, for you have already known darkness, desperation and abandonment. If you can receive it — that was a foretaste of what is to come."

Jacopone felt his own hand tremble within the shaking hand of this venerable old friar and he remembered the strange tingling sensation in hands and feet that he had experienced on his two visits to San Damiano.

He looked into the face of Leo. "Do you mean, my father, that I must make a journey to La Verna on foot as you did, and also make a spiritual pilgrimage of the heart? Must I learn the life and forgiveness of the radiant cross of San Damiano, and then enter into the darkness and pain of the cross of La Verna? And can it lead to the loving heart of God according to the pattern of Francis?"

"Francis only followed the pattern of Jesus, my brother," replied Leo. "He humbled himself to the obedience of the cross, entering into such darkness that is incomprehensible to us. There lies the mystery of our redemption, the bearing of the world's sin and the destruction of the powers of darkness."

Jacopone began to understand a little of Francis' fellowship in the sufferings of Christ as Leo went on. "If we seem to you to venerate our father Francis over much, it is not so — and he would not have it so. We look through and with our father Francis to our blessed Saviour who alone is worthy of adoration and love. The steps of the Lord Christ are those which Francis followed and thus he entered into His joy, His forgiveness, His healing.

"But he entered also into His sorrows, His tears, His rejection and darkness. If Francis lived his own Bethlehem, Nazareth and

Galilee he also entered into the Garden of Gethsemane and ascended the hill of Calvary. This is the way the Saviour went — and it is the path which we too have to follow."

As Leo spoke these words an urgent desire to know what actually happened at La Verna filled Jacopone's heart. "My father," he stammered, "now is the time. I have to know what transpired on the mountain. If I am quiet and still will you recount to me that mysterious intercourse of love that took place on La Verna?"

Leo sighed deeply and looked at Rufino, and then again at Jacopone. "See my brother," he replied, "many hours have passed as we have talked and prayed here. We have run through the hours of prayer and the other friars have been praying while we have been gossiping the day away."

"My father!" cried Jacopone. "Are you trying to hide from me, that one thing which I have to know?"

"No, my son," replied Leo. "You shall learn of it. It is a mystery not to be idly repeated, and we must cease talking now. But if you will rest and eat then we can gather with our brothers for our evening prayers. After that the three of us shall meet again and I will tell you what you need to know."

On this note Leo and Rufino rose to their feet and left Jacopone under the great oak, while the shadows lengthened and quietness wrapped him around like a great cloak.

Jacopone did not know how long he had been asleep. He was aware of a friar pulling gently upon his sleeve. "Ser Jacopone," said the habited figure, "the brothers thought it better to leave you to pray or sleep but it is getting chilly now and you have had nothing to eat since this morning. I have prepared some savoury pastries for you and some wine. When you have eaten, fathers Leo and Rufino ask you to join them in their hut." He indicated its direction.

Jacopone shook his head and yawned. He scrambled to his feet and bowed to the friar. "Thank you my brother," he said. "You are kind and I am negligent and lazy. But I will do as you say."

The friar looked at him with a certain wonder in his eyes, said something under his breath, smiled and retreated under cover of the trees.

Jacopone sat down beside the platter and bottle of wine and realised how hungry he was. He ate, drank and lay back against the tree. This was all very strange. He had the distinct feeling that changes were taking place within him. It was as if the shadows were departing from his mind and his inward vision was becoming clearer. It was not simply that he *believed* that God was leading him on — he actually *felt* it to be so! He had many things to learn, a pilgrimage to be undertaken and a vocation to be answered.

He realized now that Alberto had sent him here precisely to learn from these two holy friars, and that at some time in the future he was to make the journey to Mount La Verna. But before he could do that he must know from the mouth of Leo just what had happened to Francis on that holy mountain. He had tried to discover the truth in Todi but the friars had been uncommunicative. Either they were afraid to believe themselves, or a veil of secrecy was thrown around the last two years of Francis' life — like the veil of mist that often surrounded the mountain of La Verna in Tuscany, some one hundred kilometres away.

He shook himself out of his reverie and went to wash his face and hands in the stream. Then he retraced his steps and made for the hut which had been pointed out to him.

Dusk was turning to darkness as he drew near and when he knocked quietly there was no reply. He pushed on the door and entering in, made out the two figures of Leo and Rufino sitting motionless in the light of a single flickering candle. Behind the candle was a rough likeness of the San Damiano crucifix. Jacopone sat himself down with the others before it.

After about fifteen minutes' silence Leo began to speak. "My brother," he said, "you feel, perhaps, that your visit here over these days is ordained of God?" Jacopone nodded and listened.

"What you are to hear tonight is to be taken seriously,

reverently, lovingly — for it is the story of one who was pierced to the heart and marked in the limbs according to the wounds of Calvary. Over forty years have passed since that day and both Rufino and I are weary of this world, grieved at the betrayal of poverty in our Order and are preparing to meet our father Francis in the presence of our blessed Lord Jesus Christ.

"There are still a few tasks left in handing on the vision which Francis entrusted to us." He paused and looked in the flickering candlelight to see that Jacopone was diligent in receiving these words. Then he nodded to Rufino who took from the folds of his patched habit a leather bag containing a series of written manuscripts.

"These," he said, "contain the precious story of Francis from the lips of the early and faithful followers of his vision. They record the words of the ecstatic Giles, faithful Bernard of Quintavalle and brothers such as Masseo, Angelo, Illuminato and Silvester. We have put them together and added such as we experienced and learned ourselves from our holy father. Take them with you this night and during your remaining days with us study them prayerfully, asking any questions which may arise."

As Rufino held out the package, Jacopone was almost afraid to reach for it. He felt himself being drawn into the holy circle of those who were the initiates of a mystery, the sharers of a vision — a vision which was not to be kept secret but proclaimed and lived. It was not the message itself which had to be guarded, but its purity and pristine loveliness, for it was Francis' vision of the crucified and risen Jesus.

"There is one thing of which it were better not to speak," said Leo as Jacopone took the manuscripts and secreted them inside the lining of his *bizocone*. "I refer to the sacred happening on Mount La Verna. You are already curious about this matter and though we shall not hide it from you, you will see why it needs not to be gossiped about, for it is a thing most sacred."

As Leo began the story Jacopone felt his heartbeat quicken, for he knew that this had intimately to do with his own pilgrimage. "From San Damiano to La Verna", spoken first by

Brother Alberto and confirmed by these two survivors of the early days, was now impressed indelibly upon his heart and mind.

"You will read the details written by my hand in one of the manuscripts now in your possession," said Brother Leo. "But I will rehearse the heart of the matter to you so that you will have heard it from my lips.

"Our father Francis chose to go with him on the journey to Mount La Verna only those who were men after his own heart — Angelo, Rufino and myself. We were known as 'the three Companions'. Also with us were Sylvester, Illuminato and Masseo. We set out from the Portiuncula at the beginning of August in the year 1224, going northwards along the valley of the Tiber, through Collestrada, Citta di Castello, Monte Casale, Santo Sepolcro then west to the valley of the Arno and upwards into the heights of La Verna in Tuscany in the rising Apennines."

Jacopone watched Leo as he began the story and saw the faraway look in his eyes as he described the mountain that Count Orlando had given to Francis after hearing him preach a sermon at his castle in Montefeltro which moved his heart and changed his life.

"Francis planned to stay on the mountain from the feast of the Assumption on the fifteenth day of August until Michaelmas. The journey was hard for us all in the heat of late summer but especially for him, for he was only skin and bones.

"As we neared Tuscany we were overwhelmed by the colours and beauty of the beginnings of autumn and the rising heights of the mountainous region surrounding us. At the base of the mountains a *contadino* peasant met us and loaned his donkey to Francis for the last part of the journey, saying to him, 'Let me give you some good advice. It is that you should be as good as your word, for you have a great reputation among us.' Francis immediately struggled down from the donkey and kissed the man's feet with gratitude."

Leo seemed to withdraw into himself as he described the long and arduous climb of 1300 metres, with the singing birds settling on Francis' shoulders.

"On the spur of the mountain there is an enormous fissure," he continued, "plunging deep down the widening at the lower level. Here Francis settled his cell and bid the rest of us dwell simply in our own hermitages."

Leo's voice lowered almost to a whisper as he recalled the words of Francis: "Brother Leo, I feel that death is not far away. I want to be alone with God in sorrow for my sins and in longing for His love. Will you bring me a little bread and water and guard my solitude so that no-one else comes near?"

"Then he retired to his hut of branches," continued Leo, "leaving it only to sit sometimes under the great beech tree there and gaze across the immense horizon which embraced the Romagna, the March of Ancona, our own Umbria, Tuscany and the whole breadth of the Italian Peninsula from the Adriatic to the Tyrrhene."

Jacopone dared to interrupt. "Did I not hear a story about that great fissure and the cataclysm which brought it about?"

Leo eyed him and smiled. "Yes, you heard rightly, Jacopo. It was said that the enormous chasm opened when our Saviour died upon the cross and cried, 'It is finished.' This story filled Francis' heart and caused him on the Feast of the Exaltation of the Holy Cross, the fourteenth day of September, to ask of God two favours which brought about the strange mystery of which I speak."

Leo looked over to Rufino who was wrapped in prayer with closed eyes. "Rufino," he said, "do you remember those two favours?"

But Rufino seemed not to be in his body and after some moments of waiting Leo went on. "Even though our blessed father had told me not to spy on him I was full of curious wonder and saw things happen during those days which filled me with awe. Especially during the nights under the light of the moon when Francis would groan and cry before God I thought of our Saviour in the Garden of Gethsemane.

"One morning, after such a night, when I had said mass for the brothers, Francis asked me to open the Gospel book three times, as he sometimes did in order to hear God's word. However I tried to make the book open at different places, each time it spoke of the passion of Christ. By this Francis knew that his two favours were to be granted."

"But what were they?" cried out Jacopone who now felt the dark mystery enveloping him. Leo answered in continuing the story.

"Just before the rising of the sun on that feast of the Holy Cross our father Francis knelt before his hut, facing east, and cried out with tears, 'Lord, I ask two favours of You before I die; first, to experience in my body, as far as possible, the very sufferings of Your cruel passion, and then to feel in my soul the very love which moved You to sacrifice Yourself for us.' And lost in tenderness and pity he continued to weep and pray in this manner."

As Leo said these words a quiet groaning and weeping came from the still form of Rufino, and motionless with his eyes closed he seemed to be speaking from afar: "Then from the height of heaven a seraph having six wings of flame swept down towards him. Between the pairs of wings was our crucified Saviour on His cross, who fixed blessed Francis with His burning gaze, imprinting on his dear body the marks of His sacred passion — the stigmata of the crucifixion . . . hands to hands . . . feet to feet in love . . . and heart to heart in one great stab of pain . . ." and his voice subsided and his quiet weeping trailed off into silence.

Jacopone felt a shuddering fear take hold of him, and though both Leo and Rufino were perfectly still he felt a profound communion of pain and love that caught up the three of them into its throbbing glory.

For fully half an hour they remained in stillness, with no word spoken but aware of a shared love and wonder such as Jacopone had never experienced before.

Then at last Leo opened his eyes. "My brother," he said, "all this is written in the manuscripts I have given you — and more than this concerning the sacred wounds. Although our father Francis sought to hide them yet we who were near him and later nursed him saw and touched and wondered and adored."

Then a distinct change came over Leo. He took a deep breath, breathed out slowly and spoke in a voice which was his own and yet which communicated prophetic power: "My son Jacopone," he said, "at Mount La Verna you will meet My servant John. Listen to him. Hold to him. Let your soul be joined to his, for he will lead you into the way of Francis and into the way of My Love. In life and death he will be your friend. Do not forsake him."

Leo then shook his head, hardly aware that he had been speaking, and continued in his normal voice: "Take the writings now. Lose yourself in them for as long as you need, and when the time comes you will know what to do. Remember only one thing. The journey from San Damiano to La Verna is long and arduous, but one which you must then undertake in love."

Jacopone placed his hand upon the manuscripts in his inner pocket and understood the importance of Leo's intention to share with him in prayer, in words and in writing the primitive and ecstatic vision vouchsafed to Francis — so that it might continue in its pristine loveliness and austere simplicity.

He spent the next three days at the Portiuncula, eating and sleeping sparingly, but reading, thinking praying and seldom questioning. He could get no more information from Brother Leo concerning the mysterious John of whom he had spoken. Indeed when Jacopone brought the matter up Leo looked somewhat quizzically at him and made no answer.

So on the evening of the third day he returned the manuscripts to Brother Leo and embraced the two companions. Then with Leo's hands of blessing upon his head he returned to Todi to await the moment of God's choosing.

6 The Secret of the Stigmata

Back in Todi, Jacopone was restless. His thoughts constantly roamed back to the Portiuncula and the vision of the early and pure days of Franciscan life which Leo and Rufino had shared with him. His restlessness urged him to action, but until the sign came he could not know what the action was to be.

So during the next months he continued his ascetic life of discipline. He moved out of his stripped house in Todi and lived in a simple hut in the corner of one of his former orchards. This was the base for his ministry of preaching, singing and evangelizing around the villages and towns of Umbria.

It became a common sight to see Jacopone and his donkey, with his knapsack on his back and his lute strung across his shoulder. There were still times when certain people taunted him with *"Pazzo! Pazzo!"* as he climbed up to the tiny towns and villages perched on the sides of the Umbrian hills. But his call to repentance and faith and his strange ways of acting and speaking reminded the ordinary people of the stories of the prophets depicted on church frescoes and expounded by the *zelanti* and the Dominican friars. They listened spellbound to his stories and sang the songs which he composed and set to local Umbrian folk tunes, celebrating the Gospel life of austerity, simplicity and love.

On one such day he was preaching in the market place in Todi, telling the story of the rich young man who yearned to follow Jesus, but could not let go his money and property.

As he came to the end of his homily he was aware that he was being observed by one of the sympathetic *mitigati* friars from San Fortunato. Jacopone's voice carried over the heads of the crowd. "Turn away, rich young man," he cried. "Turn away from the Christ who loves you, from the Lord who became incarnate for you, from the Saviour who is crucified for you — but turn away too from peace, from joy, from light and from love . . ." Brother Giorgio felt the power of such impassioned and sincere preaching — popular but not vulgar — and he remembered earlier days when the Gospel had sounded as clear and challenging in his ears and heart.

He waited as Jacopone counselled and prayed with some penitents, while the crowd joined with the tertiaries in singing one of his songs to a lively traditional love-tune:

> *Jesus, Lover, dear and fair,*
> *Great are You, beyond compare.*

Your strong love will never leave us,
Though we sin, You will forgive us,
Crowned with glory You'll receive us,
    If our cross we humbly bear.

Jesus, Lord, we kiss Your feet,
Manna is not half so sweet,
Never leave us, we entreat,
    Orphaned of Your pitying care.

On the cross You clearly show
Love that does embrace us so,
Love that dragged You down so low,
    Crucified in anguish there.

Love so deep, so high, so great
Makes the heart inebriate,
Leaving all to contemplate
    You, my Lord, so wondrous fair.

Gazing on the Only Pure,
All the world seems but a lure,
And a madness with no cure,
    From its snare deliver us.

> *Jesus, Lover, dear and fair,*
> *Great are You, beyond compare.*

"You've really got them going today, Jacopone," remarked Giorgio as Jacopone approached in response to his beckoning.

"*We* do not seem to get such results — but then we don't preach like you!"

Jacopone felt a bitter retort rise to his lips but caught himself in time. After all, Giorgio was being appreciative — more than most of the *mitigati* friars, who treated Jacopone as a buffoon.

"I tell you, Giorgio," he replied, "I find more faith in an ordinary peasant woman here in the market place than in many of those fat friars from Bologna or those boring learned friars from Paris. And remember this — nobody believes a fat monk!"

"Yes," laughed Giorgio. "I heard that was your text last week. The *relaxi* brothers were not so relaxed when they heard that!"

"Well, let them shift their overfed carcasses and complain to me," retorted Jacopone, "and I'll strip a few pounds from them."

"I think they'd prefer to criticize from a distance," said Giorgio good naturedly. "But I'm forgetting my message. Brother Alberto wants you to come to the convent as soon as you can — he has some news from the Portiuncula."

Jacopone stopped and caught his breath. At the word Portiuncula he felt as though he had been smitten on the chest, and the colour drained from his face.

"Are you all right?" asked Giorgio, taking his arm.

"Oh yes," replied Jacopone quickly, trying to recover himself. "It's just that . . . oh never mind, I'm all right now, let's go!"

So they went together to San Fortunato and Jacopone was admitted to the cell where Alberto awaited him.

The Guardian rose from his writing table to greet his guests with a somewhat serious smile upon his face. "Jacopone," he said, "sit down, will you? I have received some news which has caused me grief and will sadden you too."

Jacopone felt something of that shadow fall over him again as he sat and listened to Alberto. "I'm sorry to tell you that one of the *Portiuncula* friars has come with the news that dear Brother Rufino had some kind of a fit a day or two ago which left him without speech, and early this morning he closed his eyes in death."

Jacopone crossed himself, murmuring *"Requiescat in pace"*, and slumped forward, his head in his hands.

"I fear we are coming to the end of the second chapter in the history of our Franciscan Vision," said Alberto quietly. "Only Leo is left now, and from what the friar said today it looks as if he is preparing for that journey too.

"There is a strange story accompanying the news. Apparently about a week ago the two friars had a presentiment of death. Leo had a dream in which Bernard of Quintavalle came to him, telling him that he was soon to be quit of his body and enter into the nearer presence of our Lord. When he told Rufino in the morning, Rufino replied that Bernard had come to him too — though not in a dream but in a waking vision. He had said that he was also to be taken, but that the vision had priority over the dream."

Jacopone smiled in spite of his sorrow. "Yes," he murmured, "it seemed to me that they were so in harmony with one another that one would not be able to remain long without the other."

Alberto looked keenly into Jacopone's face, for he had heard him preach somewhat austerely on detachment from creatures in such a way as to disparage human relationships and especially particular friendships.

Jacopone understood the implication of Alberto's glance. "Yes my brother," he said sadly. "I have been wrong about many things. Being at the Portiuncula taught me much about detachment, asceticism and discipline. What you told me with your lips these two friars lived out in their lives. They lived in love without lust, they used simple things without avarice and they practised poverty without affectation. They followed the way of Jesus and Francis for love's sake, and not for the sake of ascetic virtues. But where does that leave me?"

Alberto's face radiated joy in spite of his grief. "If you are learning these things, my brother," he said, "you are learning the evangelical way. It is the royal road to holiness. I suppose these next few months will confirm you in that way and prepare you for that which is to come."

Jacopone looked up quickly. "What do you mean, father?" he asked.

"I speak to you bluntly," replied Alberto. "I mean that Leo will die soon and that his death will convey to you some clear word of guidance. Do you take my meaning?"

"I do," said Jacopone. "I see that my pilgrimage and search for Francis has only just begun. It is not simply a search for Francis but for Christ in His fullness."

Without another word Alberto led Jacopone to the convent chapel and, kneeling before the reserved sacrament, all that had passed before them in conversation was confirmed and rooted in their hearts. Then Jacopone took his leave.

And so it was. Leo remained only a few months — as if to console his brothers for the loss of Rufino and to reassure them in the shadow of his own passing.

"Do not hinder me any longer," he was reported to have said. "Our blessed father Francis said, 'Welcome, sister Death' when the physician from Arezzo told him of his fatal condition. He asked Brother Angelo and myself to sing the *Canticle of the Sun* to him. Rufino has preceded me, but now my turn has come."

Jacopone remembered the stanza that St Francis had added when Leo and Angelo sang at his death bed:

By death our Sister, praised be,
From whom no one alive can flee.
Woe to the unprepared!
But blest be those who do Your will
And follow Your commandments still.

Thus one morning, after spending what seemed an inordinate amount of time in ecstasy after saying mass, Leo slipped into unconsciousness with that stanza upon his lips, surrounded by the weeping friars who had realized the import of this man's passing. The last vital link with Francis had gone and they felt bereft and heavy of heart.

This was the call that Jacopone had been waiting for! He had done his sorrowing at the death of Rufino. It was then that he grieved for them both, knowing that he would see neither of them on earth again. With the death of Leo came the sign to make the pilgrimage, for it was clearly in their minds that he should make the journey when the sign was given. And quite apart from the importance of that place in the sharing of the vision, he was curious to meet the Brother John whom Leo had mentioned but about whom he had been somewhat reticent and vague.

Jacopone understood from his time at the Portiuncula that this outward journey "from San Damiano to La Verna" was the sign and symbol of the interior pilgrimage, and that without the geographical journey the interior pilgrimage could not be undertaken. So he set off.

It was late autumn when he began the journey, and he followed the way that the early friars had taken with St Francis back in 1224, forty-seven years before, passing through or around many of the villages and towns in which he himself had preached. There were some very cold nights and plenty of mist and rain in the days, but he avoided staying with tertiary and penitent friends on the way. Instead he travelled in silence and prayer, sleeping in barns and covered outhouses, though sometimes begging a bed from a stranger.

This journey on foot, begging his food and shelter, turned out to be a difficult journey, relieved on some days by a glorious watery sun and melancholy sunsets over high mountains, and amidst glorious bursts of colour in the northern parts of Umbria and into Tuscany. It was December before he reached the base of the holy mountain.

La Verna was sharply distinguished by its height and curious formation, and at this time of year was covered with snow on its upper reaches. Jacopone climbed through the moss and twisted trees, stumbling among the masses of broken limestone, and as he beheld for the first time that striking fissure of which Leo had told him it stirred in him a sense of wonder at the mystery and suffering of Christ's death.

He knew that he could only have made this journey when the right time had come, and now he realized that the deaths of Rufino and Leo answered the inward movement of his own spirit. He, and they, were caught up in something bigger than themselves — and it had to do with this place.

As he stumbled upward among the limestone rocks a friar came down, barefoot among the stones and flurries of snow which blew from the top of the mountain. Jacopone was comforted by this messenger of welcome, who seemed to know who he was and why he had come. He greeted Jacopone gently but warmly and led him to a crude but adequate hut of branches and wood, welcoming him to the small group of friars who shared the life of prayer on La Verna.

The mountain had been made holy by the holiness of Francis, and especially by the mysterious happening called the stigmata, in which Francis had been pierced in hands, feet and side by the crucified Jesus who had manifested himself to him, as Leo had told Jacopone. When Francis had commended La Verna into the care of the first Companions he had said to Brother Masseo: "Brother Masseo, I desire that the Superiors only send here brothers who love God and are among the best of the Order."

So, on that first evening of what was to be six months of contemplation and silent manual work the friars, with their Guardian Mario at their head, took Jacopone into their life. After the first simple supper they relaxed the rule so that they could talk together.

Jacopone was firstly concerned about access to the life of contemplative prayer and progress in his pilgrimage, and to this end he asked Brother Mario if they had some written sources of the life of Francis.

Five years previously the General Chapter of the Order, meeting in Paris, had outlawed all but the "official" life of St Francis — the *Vita* written by Brother Bonaventure the

Minister General — and this was a stylized biography, a kind of expurgated version with all the follies, sins and eccentricities of the saint removed. As such it was unacceptable to the *zelanti* party of Spirituals and to many other friars in the Order.

In answer to Jacopone's question Mario replied: "Yes, Ser Jacopone. We have the *Vita* written by Brother Bonaventure when he was Minister General." Jacopone frowned. Mario gave a wry smile and continued, "And we have the *Vita Prima* and the *Vita Secundum* of Brother Thomas of Celano."

"Yes, yes," retorted Jacopone with a trace of impatience, "but do you have any of the writings of the first Companions, especially the collection written by Brothers Leo, Angelo and Rufino from the Greccio hermitage, which they described 'as from a fair meadow to pluck a few flowers which seemed the most beautiful'?"

"Ah yes, the *Fioretti*," replied the Guardian quietly, making sure that no-one else was in earshot. "Well, Ser Jacopone, you know of the suppression by the General Chapter of all but the *Legenda Maior* of Bonaventure, and of the decree that all other manuscripts should be destroyed?"

"Yes, I know that well," answered Jacopone, hardly controlling his anger, "but I do not suppose you allowed that to happen here, father?"

"That is not the sort of question I usually invite," replied Mario, "but you know of our relationship with the early Companions and the mind of Brother Leo in all this. And I am aware of the special relationship which existed between you and the two friars at the Portiuncula — may they rest in peace."

He made the sign of the cross upon himself and continued: "I have, apart from what I have mentioned, a fair number of scrolls containing the writings you request as well as some others you may not have seen. You are welcome to a secret perusal of them all."

Jacopone voiced his gratitude and bowing his head he beat on his breast with a clenched fist. "I am sorry I allowed anger to rise just now, but the *litterati* of Paris seem not only to monopolize the interpretation of our holy father's will and intentions but to suppress and destroy all others. I am grateful to you for your trust and generosity, my father."

Then he looked at Mario and said: "May I also ask if there are among your collection, the *Five Considerations on the Stigmata?*"

"Where else would they be?" asked Mario with a smile. "And who else but you would be asking such a question just now?"

Jacopone looked deeply into Mario's eyes, but the Guardian did not flinch, then he answered Jacopone's look. "I cannot answer now the questions which I can see in your eyes, but I do believe that we are both caught up in the mystery which is the secret of this holy mountain. If you will be patient, wait in prayer and quietly work with your hands, then I believe a work of grace will be done in you which will lead you in the direction you must go.

"The mystery of the wounds of Calvary is not spoken of openly here, but it is treasured among us in silence and prayer. I ask you not to exhibit an inordinate and inappropriate curiosity before the other friars. What you need to know will be given you by the Holy Spirit in due time."

Jacopone reddened and fell to his knees. "Yes my father. I only begin to understand, but it is not from man that I seek to learn. Forgive what must seem a rash boldness before such a mystery. I would ask your blessing now — but one more question before I do. Do you have here a Brother John with whom, with your permission, I could speak?"

Mario looked puzzled and then said, "It is strange that you mention that name. We have had no John here in my memory but I have dreamed of such a one. I think perhaps he is not yet — but is to come."

"He is not yet," repeated Jacopone. "I wonder if that was the reason why Leo was so vague and mysterious about him? I shall have to wait."

He remained upon his knees while Brother Mario blessed him and made upon him the sign of the holy cross.

Jacopone spent six months of alternating light and darkness at La Verna, giving his mind to study, his heart to love and prayer and his body to manual work. In spite of his disdain for the *litterati* friars with their prizing of the intellectual life, he used his mind and practised calligraphy to copy out much of the written matter entrusted to him. He also composed many poems and songs of devotion and prayer.

He wandered around the holy mountain and spent many hours in solitary prayer, sharing with the friars in their liturgy and mass, occasionally taking his meals with them, but mostly eating sparingly and alone. So the months passed until Holy Week. With the first warm currents of spring upon the high mountain the shadow of Calvary enshrouded Jacopone's soul and he felt a presentiment of revelation as the day of crucifixion drew near.

On Holy Thursday he went to the mass of the Lord's Supper in the friars' chapel and was deeply moved when brother Mario removed his mass vestment and girded himself with a towel. He then knelt before the brothers and washed their feet, kissing each foot in turn as Jesus had done in the Upper Room before His passion.

There was no mass on Holy Friday, only the bare chapel, the bleak psalms of dereliction, with no note of music or chant.

The friars spent the three hours of the passion together in liturgical prayer and silence, but Jacopone made his way to an advanced spur of rock which fell away before him for hundreds of metres — the place where Francis was said to have knelt on the Feast of the Holy Cross in 1224.

He recalled what Leo had said as he knelt down on the bare rock. "Our holy father Francis," he murmured, "asked for two favours. First that he should feel in his body as far as may be possible the sufferings of Christ's passion; and second, that he should be moved with the very love which caused Christ to suffer for the sins of mankind." He dared not use such words for himself but found himself bewildered and confused by such a prayer.

He saw himself in imagination in the Garden of Gethsemane, shivering in company with Peter, James and John, the three chosen disciples. Then he felt himself to be there alone as the shadow of the cross fell upon the Saviour's heart.

How long he remained in prayer he did not know, but when he came to himself he found that he had slipped down from his knees on to his face, and was prostrate upon the ground. A light wind was blowing and as the feeling came back into his body he experienced again that tingling of hands and feet, that burning in his chest that he had felt before at San Damiano.

It was not pain and he was not overwhelmed by vision or revelation, yet he became very conscious of an interior voice which said, "My son Jacopone, it is a long journey from San Damiano to La Verna. The first part of your pilgrimage is complete. Now learn well the lessons My servants Leo and Rufino have taught you. Ponder deeply the wounds My lover Francis bore in My likeness, and learn humbly and patiently the way of the cross . . ."

Then there was silence. The light wind whispered through the leaves and grasses. And there came upon Jacopone a peace and tranquillity which calmed his fears, took the bitterness out of his pain and seemed to be the antidote to his madness and anger. Jacopone wondered that Christ had dealt with him so gently, so tenderly. He remained where he was until the *Ave Maria* bell sounded, and then he returned to his hut.

On holy Saturday, in a stillness of body and mind, he walked in silence around the slopes of La Verna, wondering how the world could put forth buds and leaves while the Lord of Life lay cold in his tomb.

He stayed on the mountain for two more months — then with the blessing of Brother Mario he took his leave.

7 Obedience and Surrender

After returning from La Verna Jacopone took up his itinerant ministry of preaching and singing with renewed energy. He became a troubadour for God throughout the Marches of Ancona and continued to evangelize the villages and towns of Tuscany and Umbria. Whenever he felt moved by the Holy Spirit he found caves in the hills where he spent weeks and sometimes months in prayer and solitude. After some time he felt moved again to preach and sing of the love of Christ in the market places, calling people to repentance and teaching them to sing of penitence and love, of grief for sins committed and joy for sins forgiven.

Seven years passed, and it was an ascetic and somewhat gaunt Jacopone that emerged, in contrast to the fastidious, full-fleshed lawyer of his pre-conversion days. But one day he was arrested in his tracks by a stinging rebuke from a *mitigati* friar near Montefalco. And it turned his world upside down again!

It was on the road from Foligno to Montefalco that the incident took place. The hottest part of the summer day was over and a light breeze had a refreshing effect upon Jacopone as he strode briskly along. He had spent some days giving teaching and counsel to the loosely organized tertiaries in and around Foligno who looked to the *zelanti* friars for spiritual help. Jacopone was himself a tertiary but his gifts of evangelism and spiritual counsel were valued highly and his influence was felt beyond the confines of the *zelanti* or Franciscan groups.

Over the last few years he had been caught up in what seemed to be the widest extremes of religious experience. Sometimes inebriated with the love of Christ he wandered around Umbria and central Italy driven by the *santa pazzia*, the holy madness of divine love. This gave a certain edge to his preaching as he acted out in prophetic symbolism the poverty and compassion of Christ. His name and fame spread far abroad and he had only to appear on the outskirts of a town for children, peasants and townsfolk to surround him — all prepared for the Spirit to strike them down in the anguish of penitence, leading to confession, conversion and ecstatic joy.

Then there were times when a great stillness would steal over Jacopone and he would make off to some cave or hut in the mountains or woods for months on end. There he would wrestle sometimes with his madness, sometimes with his yearning for the love of God; and sometimes he was afflicted by a certain emptiness, dryness and inability to communicate.

It was not long after such a period of aridity and restlessness that he came face to face with Brother Sebastiano, who was coming from the direction of Todi, via Montefalco, bearing some message from the San Fortunato convent.

Jacopone would have liked to have passed him by without a word for he was in no mood to make pious conversation with a *mitigati* friar whom he secretly despised. But Sebastiano felt otherwise.

"Greetings to you, Jacopone!" he cried. "I blinked twice when I saw you, for you have changed greatly since the day you sought admission among the donkeys of San Fortunato. I suppose you have been fasting and praying with great fervour!"

Jacopone thought that the discipline of some asceticism would do Sebastiano a great deal of good, but he suppressed such uncharitable thoughts as he replied, "I suppose we all change, brother. But the change which is most necessary is that of true conversion."

"Oh, can't you lay off preaching for a season?" grinned Sebastiano. "This is a day which is to be enjoyed without the aid of homilies and moralizing. I get enough of that in the convent."

Jacopone permitted himself a smile. "Perhaps you ought to practise your rule and not only give ear to it."

"And perhaps you ought to have the discipline of a rule to live by, instead of always pleasing yourself." retorted Sebastiano.

Jacopone stiffened and fixed Sebastiano with his clear gaze. "What do you mean by that?" he demanded.

"I mean what I say," replied Sebastiano. "For the last ten years your style of life has attracted all the attention you wanted. The people of Todi felt sorry for you in your bereavement — and that includes the friars at the *mitigati* convent. But from then on you played it well — mixing distraught madness with a claim to prophetic power. Your preaching was too fervent for us, just like the hysterical behaviour of some of the mad mendicant groups. The flagellants did it in their way — and you certainly do it in yours!"

By now Jacopone had become white with anger. The lashing of Sebastiano's tongue had the effect of a whipping on his bare back. Not only did he feel anger rise within him but he was alarmed by his intense desire to lay Sebastiano on his back in the dust. The "old Adam" had sprung to his defence and it took him all his powers to control the shuddering rage that was welling up within him. On top of all this he found that he, who was never without a word for any situation, seemed to have been struck dumb in the face of the *mitigati's* onslaught.

Sebastiano noticed the effect his words had upon Jacopone. He moved out of his path, pulled his habit around him, and as he set off towards Foligno he said, "That seems to have shaken you up a bit, Jacopone! I recall you once preaching on the story of the Prodigal Son when you placed the *mitigati* friars in the role of the elder brother. Perhaps you had better think again about the younger one — independence, stubborn pride, arrogance and the desire to selfishly go your own way. Maybe it's time you performed a new penance — such as returning to your father!"

So saying, he grinned again and swung away along the dusty road, leaving Jacopone shocked and shivering at this revelation of his true condition.

He picked his way up into the hills above Montefalco and found the cave he sometimes used for prayer and retreat. For the next week, hardly eating or sleeping, he lived in the realization that a revelation from God had come through the mouth of a *mitigati* friar, and this humbled and prostrated him.

As the next few days went by he realized that his old worldly arrogance had not died. It had put on a pious garment but still dominated his thinking. In spite of the hard penance he had inflicted on his body, in spite of the real joy of absolution and forgiveness, in spite of the experiences of vision and love which he felt had been granted him in prayer, his *will* was still not totally given to God. Far from total submission, Jacopone realized that he was still as heady, as arrogant, as self-willed as ever he had been in the world!

He now saw his life and ministry in a new context. He was neither stupid nor ignorant and his imagination and eloquence had caused the Bible to come alive in his preaching, both to the illiterate and to the educated people who gave him ear.

In spite of his obvious material poverty he had style and charism in the eyes of his audiences, and his ascetic appearance only enhanced his reputation as a modern John the Baptist fresh from the wilderness.

This had secretly pleased him. He saw that now. All this had fed that fatal self-love which had been eating at the vitals of his soul: "That is what is wrong with me," he whispered as he lay upon the floor of the cave. "That is why I have felt such heaviness and aridity, such torpor and paralysis of body and spirit." As he thought it through he remembered that he had seen himself as heir to the old fathers of the desert, interpreting his own restlessness as their spiritual *accidie.*

With these thoughts he fell upon his face, crying out in anguish, "O God, be merciful to my sin, for it is great."

For an hour or more heaviness enveloped him, but after such crying and groaning, in order to relieve his soul and clear his mind, he took up his charcoal and a scrap of parchment from the knapsack and wrote the word *HYPOCRISY*, and underneath some lines of confession:

Very far my feet have strayed
From the road the saints have made!

Yes, far enough away, and yet I find
A coiled hypocrisy around my mind
And strive to show myself to all mankind
 With shining sanctity illuminate.

Illuminate, my lying part I play,
Heartfelt humility my false array,
Yet, unless men due honour to me pay
 At once I rage within, disconsolate.

Disconsolate my heart with all around
If one should praise with faint, uncertain sound;
But he whose praise and faith in me abound,
 In him is my delight immoderate.

Immoderate is my desire to claim
The praise bestowed upon my holy name,
But if indeed I hear a word of blame
 Straightway I turn and run precipitate.

Precipitate I run, my purpose clear
That holy in men's eyes I may appear;
Pretend, with fasts and penances austere
 I feign to spurn this world degenerate.

He thought of Sebastiano and realized what a debt he owed
him. He remembered Alberto, the Guardian of the *mitigati*
friars, and heard the words he had spoken nearly ten years
before: "I am not making a final decision about you becoming a
novice. Vocations need to be discerned and given time to
emerge . . . time for reflection and growth, for spiritual roots to
go down deep into the soil. Only after such waiting, testing and
experience will you realize what it means for your will to be
completely given to God. Then you will return . . . and we shall
see."

The remembrance of those words shook Jacopone to his

depths, and he began to moan aloud: "Oh God, I cannot enter the life of the *mitigati* friars — my place is with the *zelanti* brethren. My heart runs after total renunciation, complete abandonment, the perfect sacrifice."

But Sebastiano's voice sounded in his heart again: "Oh yes, Jacopone, see again the manifestation of self-love, the exhibitionist for whom nothing will do but the best. What are you *really* seeking? You cannot bear to be one of God's little ones, one of the friars minor. Yours is a case of inward arrogance, be it high fasting or extreme poverty. You will gain a name, earn a reputation, make your mark! Is that the pattern of the Saviour?"

It was clear to Jacopone that he wanted to tread the path of Leo and Rufino, of Giles, Bernard, Illuminato and the other Companions of Francis — the mantle of whose holiness he believed fell upon the *zelanti* friars now living in the caves and hillsides of Umbria, the Marches of Ancona and throughout central Italy.

But he was being shown another way to surrender his will — a way of greater purgation because he found it so distasteful. It would begin with him eating humble pie — going again to the door of the San Fortunato convent and simply and gently seeking admission as a beginner in the way of St Francis.

It was only after he had surrendered at this point, when at last his defences were laid low and he had said, "Your will be done", that he was filled with an inrush of unexpected joy — the joy of obedience which is better than sacrifice.

Almost at the same moment he realized that once he made this surrender and if he was accepted then he would be under the direction of Brother Alberto. It was he who had saved him from the harsh and wild excesses of his early madness and had also himself won the trust and admiration of brother Leo and Rufino.

That clinched the matter. In submission and weariness he lay down that night on his bed of bracken and slept like a little child upon the breast of its mother.

Next morning he arose just before dawn and knelt outside his cave, facing east, waiting for the rising of the sun. As the golden ball began to appear over the distant hills of Trevi, that beautiful little town which clung to the side of the mountain, he cried out: "Hail, Sun of Righteousness, risen with healing in Your wings; shine on me and dispel the darkness and gloom of my soul; fill me with the radiance of Your glory and lighten all the dark places of my heart."

Then after some minutes of stillness he cried again: "I will arise and go to my father and I will say to him, 'Father, I have sinned against heaven and before you, and am not worthy to be called your son; make me one of your hired servants.'"

So the joy of penitence laid hold on Jacopone and, weak in body as he was, he dipped himself naked in the mountain stream near his cave. Then, wrapping his tattered *bizocone* around himself, he went tumbling and stumbling down the hill, skirting the town of Montefalco, making his way back to Todi — thus to embrace the second great crisis of his life.

It was his intention to make the journey in two days, but by the afternoon of the first day he found himself stumbling along the hot and dusty road, engulfed by waves of nausea. He managed to pull himself aside from the road, falling against the post of a gate where he was found less than half an hour later by the woman of the house as she returned from Montefalco in her donkey and trap.

Signora Margarita turned him over on to his back. She was no timid peasant girl but a woman of middle age and a fellow tertiary who had been converted under the powerful preaching of Jacopone some three years previously. As she caught sight of his face, she cried: "Oh, Jacopone — the fool of love!"

Hurrying into the house she rounded up her husband and two labourers, and soon Jacopone was stripped, bathed, warmed and beginning to take some nourishing broth and milk.

Signora Margarita had diagnosed his condition by his gaunt appearance and emaciated body.

She took him firmly in hand. Jacopone was not allowed to leave the smallholding until he could give a good account of himself both in body and spirit, though he was restless to be on his way from the moment he recovered from his faint.

In Margarita he found a woman who did not assault his sensuality as some women had done over the past few years, for she was a matron. But he found a firm and feminine human being before whom he could unburden himself and who understood why he was in such a state. She possessed the gifts of discernment and humour and helped him see that there was no need for anxiety or haste but that he was to respond to God's leading in a tranquil and gentle manner, living each moment within the love of God.

"Mother Margarita," he asked her one evening as they fed the poultry together, "how is it that after so short a time in the life of faith you have so surpassed me in understanding and love?"

"It is not a matter of understanding, Jacopone," she replied, "nor so noble a thing as love, but plain common sense. The good Lord brought you through the desolation of bereavement and broke up your old life in a mixture of madness and conversion. You needed time, space and freedom to regain your balance and to learn to trust in the love of God. He gave you many friends among the spiritual friars, and you could do no other than shout and sing His praise both in the caves and mountains of prayer and in the market places of commerce. Many of us have reason to bless God for your forceful and beautiful preaching, for to us you are the troubadour of God and the fool of love."

So saying she took him by the arm and led him into the house, seating him upon the wooden bench before the hearth. "And there is more, isn't there?" she added. "You have followed the path of our father Francis, not only in sharing the good news of

God's love but also in the desire to enter into the mystery of His pain."

Jacopone gazed at her in wonder. "How is it that you know these things about me?"

"Because I am a mother," she replied, "and because I have prayed for you every day since that blessed hour when God spoke to me through your lips. I think the time has come for you to make your way to San Fortunato. Did you know that Brother Alberto was born and brought up in Foligno? I understand well why he was able to guide you in the beginning of your new life, and I believe that he will receive you now into the community — if you will go gently."

As he looked at Margarita, Jacopone realized how much he missed the touch and love of a woman's hand and heart. He remembered that the ecstatic Brother Giles had once rejoiced when Brother Bonaventure the Minister General had told him that it is possible for a peasant woman to have more depth in love than a theologian. Margarita was no peasant woman, but she had profound wisdom.

Margarita smiled as if reading his thoughts, and went to a small corner cupboard, taking from it Jacopone's patched and laundered *bizocone*. "You will need no more clothes than those you stand in, and those my husband has willingly given you," she said, "but you might like to wear this along the road."

Then she laughed as she continued, "I have stitched it up with prayer and it will be for you a garment of praise for the spirit of heaviness." She tossed it over to him, and he bent low as he caught it, in order to hide the tears in his eyes.

Jacopone slept well that night and next morning Margarita and the rest of the household waved him off. He did not now look like the prodigal son returning home wrecked and lonely — but he felt, perhaps for the first time in his life, a gentle penitence mixed with humility.

His knapsack provided him with simple food and drink along the road and as he walked he composed and sang of a new freedom under the rule of Christ, setting it as was his custom to an Umbrian tune which kept his feet in step:

> Faith's light and darkness in this wondrous state
> Move towards love's dawn for which I wait,
> This new wine shall break and dissipate
>   The old bottles of philosophy.
>
> Ah! where Christ is grafted on the spray,
> All the withered wood is cut away;
> See the freshness springing from decay!
>   Changing to a wondrous Unity —
>
> Love, that lives and breathes without Desire;
> Wisdom, freed from Thought's consuming fire;
> Will, at one with God, that doth aspire
>   But to obey Him in simplicity.
>
> Lo, I live! yet not myself alone;
> I am I, yet am I not mine own;
> And this change, cross-wise, obscure, unknown,
>   — Language cannot tell its mystery.
>
> Poverty has nothing in her hand,
> Nothing craves in sea, or sky or land,
> Hath the Universe at her command!
> Dwelling in the heart of Liberty.

The evening of the following day found him knocking gently at the door of the convent of the *mitigati* friars in Todi.

8 Franciscan Friar

The transition had not been easy. When the door of San Fortunato convent opened revealing to the *mitigati* friars a subdued but determined Jacopone there was both apprehension and consternation.

The threefold division among the friars of the convent which had been brought about by Jacopone's request for admittance nearly ten years before became evident again, but remarkable changes had taken place. Over the first week, while Jacopone stayed in the convent merely as a penitent, a further process of transformation became evident. This was due, largely, to the discerning and gentle influence of Alberto the Guardian.

The most surprising thing was that brother Giorgio and Sebastiano both withdrew their objections to Jacopone's admission, and under Sebastiano's influence much of the opposition collapsed, though there remained an anti-*zelanti* group of friars which, while not completely blocking his admission, viewed Jacopone's change of attitude with great suspicion.

The pro-*litterati* group had been impressed over the last few years with Jacopone's obvious intellectual status. They had discovered that Jacopone's early objections to intellectual attainments were not directed against learning as such, but against intellectual pride and achievements as a way to status or power within the Order. His own academic background and intellectual capacity were beyond reproach, and in any case, the addition of a man of Jacopone's charism and popularity to the Todi convent was not to be despised.

Jacopone was well aware of the factions within the convent, but he wisely did not either curry favour with some or rail against the lack of vision of others. He made it clear that he was of sound mind, that, from grief and a lack of spiritual maturity, he had acted extravagantly at the time of his earlier application for admission, and that he now felt an inward call to test a vocation to the life of the Conventual friars in Todi.

At the same time he did not deny that he had found help among the *zelanti* friars and made plain his belief that the robe of Francis was to be kept whole and not torn into schism by an over-zealous party spirit.

All this had been received favourably by most of the professed friars under Alberto, and at the beginning of Jacopone's second week among them the friars in Chapter voted, with some abstentions but no stated opposition, to accept Jacopone into the convent and to recommend him to profession if his novitiate proved satisfactory.

The year that followed was along the pattern laid down by Alberto. Jacopone was to stop preaching during the whole time of his novitiate, giving himself to prayer, study and manual work. The Guardian encouraged him to spend some weeks with the *zelanti* brothers in the hills around Assisi and at the Portuincula.

Jacopone was plunged into sadness when he arrived there, for the vision of brothers Leo and Rufino was so closely associated with that first holy place, and now they were gone. He spent many hours in the tiny chapel and under the oak tree where he had received his formative instruction from those two friars who were the last links in the golden chain which joined Jacopone to Francis.

He also spent some time in the Marches of Ancona where there were many scattered but zealous groups of Spirituals. It was here that he learned how much Alberto of Todi was loved by many of the *zelanti* brothers for his wisdom, discernment and controlled enthusiasm for their cause, though himself Guardian of the Conventuals. It was here also that Jacopone met Ubertino of Casale and Conrad of Offida who were both leaders among the *zelanti* friars. He also observed with some apprehension the excesses of both poverty and zeal among some of them, which manifested itself to his mind in filth and fanaticism.

On his way back to Todi he acknowledged to himself Alberto's canny wisdom in allowing him to wander freely for those weeks among the Spirituals, for it moved his own soul towards a more balanced moderation.

It was the custom to report back to the Guardian when a friar returned after some absence, and on this occasion Jacopone burst in upon Alberto, hot and dusty and without due preparation. Alberto had a young friar with him and frowned as Jacopone entered immediately upon knocking.

"Father Alberto," cried Jacopone in a rush, "do you know what some of those stupid *zelanti* friars are doing . . .?" He stopped abruptly as he saw the young friar sitting on a low stool at Alberto's feet. "I'm sorry," he stammered. "I didn't know you had someone with you."

Alberto found it difficult to be angry with Jacopone. "No, you didn't," he chuckled. "You think I wait here for your homecoming with no-one else but you in mind. I think you have not preached for so long that you are bursting with news and even perhaps with some spicy *zelanti* gossip. Brother John here will be most interested in such goings-on, for he is very fond of the Spirituals."

"Brother John?" exclaimed Jacopone with wide eyes. He looked into the flushed and smiling face of the young friar and found himself both excited and embarrassed. "I'll go away and come back when I am less hot and flustered," he said apologetically. "Would you be free in an hour, father?"

Then looking at the young friar he said: "I am sorry — sometimes I think my social graces were much more in conformity with this *mitigati* convent before I was converted!" and he put his hand over his mouth in mock sorrow for having said such a thing.

"Oh come in and sit down," said Alberto. "John here is no novice, though he is but twenty years of age — and he has been asking me about you, so it is a good time for you to meet."

Brother John of Fermo got to his feet to greet Jacopone properly, and Jacopone let himself be led to another low seat. "My brother Jacopone," said John, "I have long wanted to meet you, for your name is well known in Fermo and in the Marches of Ancona. Many are those who have been brought to conversion through your powerful preaching."

"May God grant they were converted to Him and not to me," replied Jacopone. "Thank you for your gracious greeting, young brother, But I have been full of pride and arrogance in my preaching these past years. I thought I knew so much and now I am learning that I know so little."

When Jacopone had settled down and got his breath back Alberto gently guided the conversation into a sharing of theology and experience. He was a master of this, and in these two friars, separated by nearly thirty years, he found two men of theological learning and spiritual awareness.

John told of his first ten years of infancy and childhood spent with the Benedictine canons of St Peter's, Fermo, and of his spurning of such a lax life-style and his yearning for a strong asceticism. He spoke of his reception among the friars minor at thirteen years of age and of the seven years since, spent in prayer and study, and of the deep longing in his heart to visit all the shrines and places known to Francis — leaving Mount La Verna until last.

As John mentioned La Verna, Jacopone looked at him, and for a moment their eyes met and held one another in a steady gaze. "John of La Verna," whispered Jacopone. "You must be the one . . . but so young?"

Alberto felt the powerful vibrations set up by these two souls, earnest in their love for God, and before John could take up Jacopone's words, he said, "My brothers, it seems to me that you will find it profitable to talk to one another when both of you have prepared yourselves in prayer. I suggest that you, Brother John, ask the porter-brother to take you to your cell, while Jacopone here tells me the news he was bursting to share when he disturbed us. Then after mass tomorrow you both have permission to talk as you will."

Both Jacopone and John realized the importance of the moment and the value of Alberto's counsel. As John obediently rose to leave, Alberto saw that despite their very different backgrounds and journeys, and even though there was nearly thirty years separating them in age, they were twin souls — and that this was the John of La Verna spoken of prophetically to Jacopone by Leo before he died.

"Now then, Jacopone," said Alberto when John had left, "what is it that you want to tell me?"

Jacopone seemed lost within himself for a while, and then he said, "Father, do you see what has happened? You know that Brother Leo told me to ask at La Verna for a Brother John. Could this be the one?"

"Yes," replied Alberto quietly. "But I have told you before, Jacopone, that you must greet such moments with gentleness and sensitivity, for the scripture says, 'In quietness and confidence shall be your strength.' The Holy Spirit sometimes moves in fire, but there are times when you may quench His approach by bluster and crude enthusiasm."

"I know, my father," acknowledged Jacopone with sorrow. "Both the Spirit and Brother John must be approached with sensitivity — and I am voluble and insensitive. But is it not strange that I feel such awe and wonder when I try to quieten my spirit at such times?"

Alberto smiled and laid before Jacopone one of his own stanzas which had been copied on a scrap of parchment:

O Love of the Lamb!
O Ocean calm!
Of Your depths what tongue can tell?
In you I am drowned,
For above and around
Your fathomless waters swell!
And the straightest road
To the Heart of God
Is the Swirl and the Folly of Love.

"It is difficult for you to restrain your fervour," said Alberto. "It is the glory of the primitive Franciscan vision that it produces twice-born souls like yourself. But you see in this convent that there are other sincere souls struggling to live some kind of spiritual life without the blazing passion that you have felt. Isn't this stanza from a poem of yours which you gave me before you went away?"

He took a roll of parchment from a cupboard and selected one. "Yes, here it is: *De l'Amore de Christo*... 'Of the Love of Christ on the Cross, and How the Soul Desires to Die With Him'. It is a very beautiful poem, Jacopone, and that stanza was passed on to Brother John in Fermo. He made the journey here, arriving just half an hour before you, in order to ask if you had written it and whether he could talk with you."

Jacopone looked at Alberto with wonder. "Then he *must* be the John I have been waiting for. Is it that he wants to learn from me? I feel that perhaps I need to learn from him."

"Yes, Jacopone, that is what I think too. This friar is much younger than you. He is much gentler than you. But I think he is more passionate than you, too. You will have much to learn from him. However, we shall think about that tomorrow. John will stay here for a time and then make his first journey to La Verna. I suggest that you spend some time with him while he is here, and perhaps you may follow him to La Verna after he has been there a month or two. He has permission to be away for as long a period as he feels necessary, and there are some things he needs to learn in solitude."

He led Jacopone to the door, saying, "You are too excited to tell me what you were so agitated about when you returned. I suggest you go and bathe yourself, have something to eat, and after Vespers you may return and relieve your mind of all your news so that you will be ready to talk calmly with Brother John tomorrow."

Jacopone said no more but went and did as Alberto had suggested.

Meditation followed Vespers, allowing about two hours before Compline. So Jacopone gently tapped on Brother Alberto's door and was received into a quieter and more relaxed atmosphere.

"Now, Jacopone," asked the Guardian, "what had so filled you with indignation when you crashed in here some hours ago?"

"I'm sorry about that," grinned Jacopone, "but you know me! It only goes to confirm what you have been telling me over the last months — that visions and prophecies are not to be accepted without scrutiny and theological evaluation. I now see such dangers among some of our *zelanti* brethren that it almost made me glad that I have my base here in a *mitigati* friary."

Alberto laughed out loud. "Oh do not say that," he cried. "What dramatic confrontation have you been caught up in to make you say such a thing?"

"I'm talking about the prophecies of the late Abbot Joachim of Fiore," replied Jacopone. "Some of the *zelanti* brothers have interpreted his teaching so that they are prophesying the overthrow of the ecclesiastical authorities. They also talk of a purged and holy Church being set up by the Spiritual Franciscans helped by a sprinkling of Dominican friars."

Alberto sat back in his chair while Jacopone continued in his inimitable style. "As far as I can understand it, some of our *zelanti* brethren are calling themselves the *viri spirituales*, the spiritual men of Joachim's prophecy, saying that these are the Franciscan Spirituals who shall reign with Francis during the era of the Holy Spirit which is about to dawn. They say that *zelanti* poverty is the special sign of these spiritual men, that our father Francis is the Angel of the Sixth Seal of the Book of the Revelation, and that the sixth seal is about to be broken and the ecclesiastical Antichrist to appear."

Alberto shrugged his shoulders. "Jacopone, you have heard these things before. Surely it is only a small group of extreme *zelanti* friars who have made such claims. Our saintly minister John of Parma admired the Abbot Joachim, and though he surrendered his Generalate because of his sympathies we know that these things are only matters of interpretation."

"Only interpretation?" retorted Jacopone. "There are *zelanti* friars who are not only excommunicating their brothers but enjoining the taking up of arms to bring about a political fulfilment of this prophecy. Names like Angelo of Clareno, Ubertino of Casale and the Provençal Peter John Olivi are being used by these zealots. I am afraid it will bring shame on the whole Order."

Alberto took another manuscript from his cupboard and spread it on the table. "Well, you see, Jacopone," he said, "your criticism of the Conventuals' laxity may be right and necessary, but in this context it is sensible and more objective to look at prophetic interpretation through the eyes of a Conventual friar! This manuscript is part of a sermon by Peter John Olivi. He divides the history of the Church into seven periods following Abbot Joachim's threefold division of the Ages of the Father, the Son and the Holy Spirit.

"Olivi says that there is an overlap between the fifth age of laxity and the start of the age of evangelical renewal beginning with our father Francis. He goes on to say that there will arise an Antichrist pope who will persecute the primitive rule of Francis, especially on the matter of poverty, and an Antichrist emperor who will persecute and slaughter the faithful.

"Christ will vanquish the double Antichrist and set up His kingdom on earth, ruling through the Spiritual Franciscans and the holy popes of the millenium. And all these things are imminent."

Alberto showed that he was very aware of what was happening among the political *zelanti* friars. He went on: "Peter Olivi is a good and holy man and of such intelligence and spirituality that few can stand against him, Jacopone. But he is also of such innocence that I cannot believe he would counsel political and violent action to bring in the Kingdom. If he believes these things — and it seems that he does — then he will allow the Lord to fulfil His prophecies in His own way, and without political help from the Spirituals. All this is fascinating to me, Jacopone, as I see it is to you. But what conclusions do you come to, my brother?"

Jacopone smiled grimly. "You are trying to draw me out on our recent conferences, my father. And of course you are right. It would have been counter-productive for me to have thrown in my lot with the Spiritual party, though I have many friends among the *zelanti* friars. It may be right for me to belong nominally to the Conventuals while lending my heart and hand to the Spirituals — at least to those of them who remain sane."

"Exactly, Jacopone," said Alberto with a clear firmness in his voice. "Now will this persuade you that it is time for you to move from the novitiate into the professed life of this Conventual convent? May I endorse such a request from you? Who knows — it may be that your enthusiasm, tempered with spiritual wisdom, will be the salvation of many among our *zelanti* brothers who are tempted to initiate a spiritual kingdom with carnal weapons."

He rolled up the Olivi sermon, replaced it in the cupboard and turned to look at Jacopone. "Do you know what I believe, Jacopone?" he asked. "I believe that you will continue to have an increasing following among the *zelanti* friars and that God is calling you to balance their crude emotionalism and excessive enthusiasm with an ordered life of sanctity and disciplined love. I also believe that your future is in the direction of La Verna rather than Paris, Bologna or Rome. You will be shown what to do, but the time has come for you to be professed into the one Franciscan Order and to maintain the unity of that Order for the sake of the love of God."

Jacopone bowed his head in assent and Alberto went over to him and embraced him. Jacopone had resisted the suggestion that he should be ordained a priest, but he had now sealed the decision to become a professed friar. The request to take the threefold vow was accepted by the Guardian, and the Compline bell began to ring.

Well over a year passed following Jacopone's profession as a brother in the Order of Friars Minor of Saint Francis. He showed commendable stability within the convent of San Fortunato without compromising any of his *zelanti* sympathies. Though there was still a group of *mitigati* friars who pointed to the relaxed rule, even they admitted that Jacopone was proving a more amenable brother than they had thought possible.

Giorgio and Sebastiano were now among Jacopone's firm supporters, and they had both experienced something of a conversion in their own lives. Alberto watched and presided over all these happenings with a father's heart of wisdom and love.

There were times when he felt the burden of administration and pastoral care, for it was not easy to rule with impartiality and charity when one's heart was longing for prayer and solitude. Up in the mountains of the Abruzzi above Rome there was a hermit known as Pietro da Morrone. After a life spent in founding and ruling his Benedictine monks he had retired to a life of prayer, occasionally meeting those who longed for such a life. He was known to both Jacopone and Alberto. Alberto sometimes wondered if such a life would be possible for him before he died.

Jacopone had expected to follow the young friar John to La Verna after some months. But over a year had passed and there was no word from the holy mountain.

John had spent two weeks at Todi — precious weeks of fellowship and prayer. "John," said Jacopone one evening, "what is it you are looking for at La Verna?"

"I cannot altogether say," John replied. "You know, Jacopone, that the strange mystery of the stigmata of our father Francis is not spoken of openly, but you and I have talked of it with care and in secret. What I seek is somehow linked with that mysterious sign of the cross and with the yearning for the divine Love that calls to me from your poetry and in my secret times of prayer and solitude. Can you explain to me why in your poetry and in your presence I feel such a kindling of that mystery and love that saps my strength and makes me faint with longing?"

Jacopone stared at the ground, unable to meet John's gaze, "I do not fully understand, either," he replied, "but there are two things I should tell you. First, Brother Leo spoke your name to me when I stayed with him and Rufino at the Portiuncula learning of the *zelanti* vision. He seemed to have some prophetic insight in linking us both with the pilgrimage from San Damiano to La Verna."

"Does that mean that we both have to make that journey — and do those two places have some kind of mystical meaning?" asked John.

"Yes, my brother," responded Jacopone. "Somehow we are to make up what is lacking in each other's experience, but I cannot understand how that can be. You ply me with questions and I feel I should learn from you. You have been aware of the call and mystery of God from childhood and have followed without deviation. But I have lived in sin and arrogance until I was nearly forty years of age."

"But you have known darkness and pain that would have crushed me," said John. "I shall not ask about it, for it is not time for me to know — and perhaps that is for the future too. What I do know is that I must now go on to Mount La Verna, and I believe that you will shortly follow after me."

The same fire blazed in the eyes and hearts of these two friars. They had been inexorably drawn together in fulfilment of Leo's prophecy. John burned with youthful zeal and intemperate passion of love for God, hardly knowing how it was to be channelled. He needed an older, stabilizing influence upon him — and for this he looked to Jacopone.

Jacopone recognized that he had not known such blazing first-love for God in his youth. His intemperate, passionate love for God had been spelled out in tempestuous madness and crazy foolishness following Vanna's death and his conversion. Most of this had been public. Only during the last two years had he recognized that his will also needed to be surrendered, and this had involved his entry into the Franciscan life at San Fortunato under the loving guidance of Brother Alberto.

John felt the blazing love that burned in Jacopone's heart, without recognizing the immaturity of his own emotions. Jacopone in turn saw that the young love in John needed to be tempered by mature reflection, exposure to suffering, the challenge of community life and the commitment of the will in the vows of the religious life.

Jacopone flinched at this because he saw John as the mirror of his own soul. Here he was at nearly fifty years of age, looking into the heart of a youth of twenty who could be forgiven for his lack of maturity. And what did he see? — himself as disordered, immature and lacking in the kind of wise and solid counsel that John needed. Who was to learn from whom?

Alberto watched, listened and smiled. The Lord knew what He was doing and Alberto sought simply to facilitate the work of the Holy Spirit in the lives of the friars under his care.

Brother John left Todi after the community mass one morning. He and Jacopone acknowledged the unfolding revelation which was taking place in their friendship, and with much sadness they covenanted to meet at La Verna in the will of God.

As they parted Jacopone thrust into John's hands the whole poem of which John had seen only a stanza. It represented between them the mysterious quest for the divine Love that was more understood intuitively than could be spelled out verbally. These stanzas were a sign between them of the path upon which their feet were planted. As Jacopone had repeated to John on the day that they returned from visiting the San Damiano crucifix at Assisi, "It is a long journey from San Damiano to La Verna."

John tucked the rolled parchment into the folds of his habit and felt the truth of it burning in his heart as he made his pilgrimage:

To Die for the Love of Christ

> *O Gentle Love,*
> *You died for Love,*
> *I pray You, slay me for Love!*

Love, You did lead
To death indeed,
Your Lover upon the Cross;
O tell me why
My Christ must die?
— 'Twas to redeem my loss.
Then try me by fire,
For 'tis all my desire
To die in the arms of Love.

If You did not spare
Your Beloved there,
How should I escape from You?
Your Love then took
Me with an hook,
Your fish from the sea's deep blue:
Then spare me not,
For 'tis all my thought
To perish, immersed in Love.

The Cross has lifted
Love, Heaven-gifted,
Never to let it go:
And the Cross shall take me,
Lift me, break me,
For all the world to know.
If I shrink and flee,
My name shall be
Blotted out from the Book of Love.

Lo! the world shall heed:
On the Cross I read
This scroll that in blood is writ;
That gives to me
God's own degree
In philosophy, science and wit:
And each golden line
Bears God's own sign,
Emblazoned and bordered with Love.

O Love of the Lamb!
O Ocean calm!
Of Your depths what tongue can tell?
In You I am drowned,
For above and around
Your fathomless waters swell!
And the straightest road
To the Heart of God
Is the Swirl and the Folly of Love.

9   John of La Verna

La Verna! Even the *mitigati* friars held the place in high
esteem, though most of them had little desire to make other
than a brief visit there — just to say they had seen it. But one
evening the convent at Todi was bubbling with the news that
one of the La Verna friars had arrived with a message from the
holy mountain.

Jacopone strode impatiently up and down in the vegetable
garden at the back of the convent before Compline, waiting for
the Guardian to summon him, for he felt certain that here was
the call from Brother John to come and join him on the
mountain. But no call came. Jacopone responded to the bell for
Compline and restrained himself from breaking the greater
silence, though he was too disturbed in spirit to still himself for
meditation before sleep.

Through the night his sleep was intermittent and he
constantly found himself now on the journey, now at the base of
the mountain, now in the profound stillness of the site of the
stigmata.

The convent conference took place after mass and breakfast
next morning. Brother Bruno, whom Jacopone recognized
from La Verna, sat next to Brother Alberto in the chapter room.

After the reading of the rule, the prayers and the chapter of
faults, Alberto spoke to the friars. "Brothers, last evening
Brother Bruno arrived from La Verna and apart from the
various messages and greetings which he brings, he bears news
of young Brother John who left us for his journey to the holy
mountain nearly eighteen months ago. I would not usually ask
the visiting brother to speak himself, but I think that we should
hear what Brother Bruno has to say and bear John up in our

prayers. It seems to me that a significant thing is happening at La Verna."

While Alberto was saying these words Jacopone had become more restless, feeling the import of the message and anxious to know in his mind what he already felt in his heart. He tried to keep still and to listen intently as Bruno spoke.

"My brothers," began Bruno. "You, of all friars, do not lay great store by visions, locutions and the like. And it must be admitted that such claims to signs and wonders need to be tested by Scripture, by the fathers of the Church and by the common mind of the Order. But our Guardian, Brother Mario, feels that there is happening at La Verna a deepening of the sense of the presence of our father Francis and a renewing of the vision which God vouchsafed to him.

"Because our holy father thought of La Verna as a special place of prayer and contemplation we believe that the favours which we are experiencing there in the manifestation of God's grace will overflow to all parts of our Franciscan Order and will sanctify our prayer and work at every level."

Some of the friars shifted uneasily in their places, somewhat suspicious of such spiritual talk, for it led, as they often said, either to exaggerated asceticism on the one hand or to inflamed emotionalism on the other. Neither of these built up the community in its work or witness.

"Tell us," said Sebastiano, whose attitude had undergone a considerable transformation since Jacopone's admission to the convent, "what do you mean by the favours of God's grace to which you refer?"

"This involves our Guardian's message and request to you brothers here at San Fortunato," continued Bruno. "The beginning and continuance of these things is centred in Brother John.

"When he came to us from you some eighteen months ago he impressed us with his quietness of spirit. He seemed to us to be a youth consecrated from his mother's womb, brought up for the first years of his life with the Benedictine canons. Seeking a more ascetic and evangelical way he took the habit of our Order when only thirteen years old. He seemed also to be free from pride, pettiness and extremes of every kind, seeking only a simple life of prayer, manual work and the love of God."

As Bruno continued the friars quietened themselves and were taken up in the spell woven by his simple charm. Jacopone, while maintaining an outward composure, felt his heartbeat pounding through his body, and given different circumstances, would have thrown himself to the ground, groaning and weeping for the love of God. But he sat and listened.

"One day, about six weeks after his arrival," said Bruno, "the Novice Guardian Gianfranco preached the homily at our Sunday mass. He spoke of the inner meaning of La Verna and the mystery of dying to self or self-naughting, which some of the holiest of our friars maintain is the entrance porch to the secret of the divine Love.

"Suddenly Brother John fell from his place on to the floor of the chapel and began weeping, though softly and gently. The strange thing was that Gianfranco went on preaching, though in slower and reverent voice, accompanied by the quiet sobbing of Brother John.

"The rest of us did not go to his aid but left him there. Somehow it was all contained and no-one was alarmed. Indeed, the feeling spread without undue emotion and from that day there has been a new spirit of fervent love, of common charity and of zeal for God among the brothers."

Some of the Todi friars were unsettled by this account, but because of the manner of Bruno's telling they said nothing.

"And this John of Fermo," went on Bruno, "is suddenly and often seized by what seems to be a spiritual inebriation. When God, Christ or the divine Love is spoken of, his heart melts like wax and he cannot contain himself, kindled by the Holy Spirit. There are times when he runs to and fro upon the mountain, weeping, singing, praying, and seems indeed to dwell in the loving embrace of our Saviour."

"The *jubilus*," muttered Jacopone from his place. The eyes of all the friars fixed on him as he began to chant the verses of his own poem on the *jubilus*, trying to express that frenzy of spiritual joy which often breaks out in incoherent cries — a result of the excessive fire and love enkindled by the Holy Spirit in the beginnings of the mystical life.

His chanting was so powerful, following upon the moving account by Brother Bruno, that all present, from Brother Alberto down to the youngest novice, were constrained to listen in wonder:

> *You, Jubilus, the heart will move*
> *And make us sing for very love.*

The *Jubilus* in fire awakes
　　And straight the man must sing and pray;
His tongue in childish stammering shakes,
　　Nor knows he what his lips may say;
　　He cannot quench nor hide away
　　　　That Sweetness pure and infinite.

The *Jubilus* in flame is lit,
　　And straight the man must shout and sing;
So close to Love his heart is knit,
　　He scarce can bear the honeyed sting;
　　His clamour and his cries must ring,
　　　　And shame for ever take to flight.

The *Jubilus* enslaves man's heart,
　　— A love-bewildered prisoner —
And see! his neighbours stand apart,
　　And mock the senseless chatterer;
　　They think his speech a foolish blur,
　　　　A shadow on his spirit's light.

So, when you enter deep the mind,
   Jubilus, you rapture fair,
The heart of man new skill will find
   Love's own disguise to grasp and wear,
   The suffering of Love to bear,
     With song and clamour of delight.

And thus the uninitiate
   Will think that you are crazed indeed;
They see your strange and fevered state,
   But have not wit your heart to read;
   Within, deep-pierced, that heart may bleed,
     Hidden from curious mortal sight.

There was silence when Jacopone had finished. Judging the time to be right, Alberto spoke to the assembled friars. "Now, my brothers, you have heard, in ways impossible for me to communicate, what is happening at La Verna. I know some of you will want to greet it with caution and subject it to careful scrutiny. But I would ask you to be open in your hearts, for nothing unworthy or excessive is being claimed. I feel in my heart that if Brother Mario seeks our prayers in this matter, he is entrusting us with a treasure, and lays upon us a responsibility. I think we should not now open this conference for discussion for it would but kill what we have heard, and perhaps grieve the Holy Spirit."

As he looked around upon the twenty or so friars assembled he saw that some of them were filled with an awe which showed upon their faces, and some of them nodded in silent agreement with their Guardian's words. But even those who would usually have put up a lively argument against any signs of emotionalism or franticism kept their own counsel. They felt it was not appropriate to disturb the powerful feeling which had been evoked in the conference — a feeling they had not experienced before!

As the assembly broke up with prayer Alberto motioned to Jacopone to accompany him and Brother Bruno to his cell.

When the door closed behind them the three friars together fell upon their knees before the image of their crucified Lord. After some minutes of silence Bruno quoted another stanza which extolled the madness of love:

For since God's wisdom, though so great
    Is all intoxicate with love,
Shall mine not be inebriate,
    And so be like my Lord above?
No greater glory can I give
    Than sharing His insanity.

Alberto then got to his feet and looked at the other two. "Now, brothers," he said, "calm yourselves and set your minds to this matter. You see how much I wanted our friars here of the *mitigati* to catch the feel and power of what is happening at La Verna. But you see also that if you press your case too hard you will alienate their sympathies. Our Lord says we are to be 'wise as serpents but harmless as doves', and so I thought it wise to conclude our meeting when I did. But now, Jacopone, since you are so intimately involved in all this, you must listen to what Brother Bruno has to say."

Jacopone did not reply but turned his face to Bruno as Alberto motioned them to sit.

"Well," said Bruno, giving his attention to Jacopone and fixing him almost severely with his eye, "it is not all intoxication and glory at La Verna. We do not run to the excesses of some of the *zelanti*."

Jacopone flinched but did not speak as Bruno continued: "In fact you must know that we have experienced outbreaks of fervent emotion often upon the mountain since the secret of our father Francis has become known. There have been some unworthy and ill-disciplined friars who have sought for lights, favours, locutions, new tongues — and even the stigmata itself.

"They have been greedy for charisms of the Holy Spirit and have become frenzied and hysterical, claiming to have received from Him special gifts. Therefore we have become adept at sifting and separating the chaff from the wheat. Those who cannot be thus separated by common sense and clear vision are soon discerned by that peculiar gift of the Holy Spirit which is God's gift to our Guardian Mario. We are neither stupid nor ill-equipped in these matters."

Jacopone shifted his position. "Yes, I remember his discernment of my impatience and pride." He smiled knowingly. "I would trust his judgement in things both temporal and spiritual."

"Following the incident at the mass homily of which I have spoken," continued Bruno, "Brother Mario called together the small council of friars who guard the holy mountain by Francis' command, and we prayed and deliberated upon the genuineness of Brother John's experience.

"We were led gently but firmly to see that it was a true expression of the kindling of the Spirit within him. But also that it was the beginning of a work which was to continue over a long period, and such beginnings often manifest an outward show of physical symptoms. The influence of your sharing and poetry upon John was noted — with approval I may say," for Jacopone looked worried for a moment. "But Mario wishes me to tell you that you must see to it that you do not stay in the beginner's path but progress in the way of holiness and discipleship."

"Would it not then be right, my fathers," cried Jacopone, "for me to join our brother John upon the mountain?" Such hope and joy glowed in his face that both Alberto and Bruno felt a certain sadness as they told him that the time was not right.

"We feel that we have in Brother John a great treasure," said Bruno with a distant look in his eyes, "and because this treasure is unsullied and not yet mature he must be guarded with love and yet given full freedom to wander and roam over the holy mountain.

"It is clear to Brother Mario and to those of us who share his oversight that John must be allowed to live out his days of wonder and glory — his *jubilus* days if you like — unhindered, with only such caution and discipline as is necessary from one guide — and that has to be our Guardian for the present. When the time comes for the Holy Spirit to lead or drive him into the wilderness then he will need counsel, care and affirmation to enter into the darkness that precedes any further progress."

"And you feel that I would be a hindrance to him in this?" asked Jacopone anxiously. "I do understand the beginnings of these things under the care of our Guardian here, and I would not stand in the way of John's pilgrimage."

"We know this," interrupted Alberto, laying his hand upon Jacopone's arm, "but the affection and solicitude that are between you both may actually lead one or other of you to remain in the place of joy and assurance when the Spirit calls into darkness and wilderness. Do you understand, Jacopo?"

But before Jacopone could answer he went on quickly: "We have called you aside to counsel and to warn you. The counsel is that you continue in loving prayer for John, for your paths are intertwined in some profound but certain manner. The warning consists not in a call to cold detachment from one another but rather that you esteem the friendship so precious that you allow one another room to grow not only in love and joy but in darkness and in the loneliness and even desolation that was necessary for our Lord, and is certainly necessary for those who are called to walk this road."

"The road that leads from San Damiano to La Verna?" asked Jacopone.

"The same," replied Bruno.

The bell for sext told them that the conversation must end. As Jacopone left them to take his place in chapel he felt both a dampening of his earlier ardour and excitement and also a strange and quiet peace, for his pilgrimage had been affirmed.

Brother Bruno left the next morning and though the life of the *mitigati* friary went on much as before there was a new sense of direction and purpose in its worship and ministry, because Bruno had left the friars with a sacred trust of prayer and love for La Verna.

Brothers Sebastiano and Giorgio drew closer to Jacopone

and he to them, though a spirit of lively debate continued to sound between them and the other brothers.

Alberto encouraged Jacopone in his various preaching escapades, his counselling among the tertiaries and his relationship with some of the *zelanti* Spirituals who were scattered over Umbria. But he also instructed him in the mystical way of prayer which involved a grounding in theology, and encouragement in a discerning and objective criticism of spiritual experience and a following in the great way laid down by the fathers of the desert and the masters of prayer. All this was based upon a deep study of the scriptures.

During this time Jacopone anxiously gathered every scrap of news he could about Brother John. The months went by until he realized that three years had passed since John had left Todi to go to La Verna. He went to see Alberto and asked him whether he was being impatient or whether perhaps the time was drawing near for him to follow John.

Alberto sighed and looked at Jacopone. "If I had not heard this week from La Verna, I would have said that your age was making you impatient for change," he chuckled. "But it seems that though Brother Mario does not invite you to stay at La Verna for any long period, he thinks it may be well for you to make a visit now, for he says that you are the one to help Brother John over the next part of his stony pilgrimage."

"Stony, did you say?" asked Jacopone. "Why, has something happened to rob John of his joy?"

"Indeed it has," replied Alberto, "but it is that something of which we spoke when Brother Bruno was here. You know that there are various dark nights through which the soul passes on its way to perfection, and it is only when a man can be trusted that he is exposed to them."

Jacopone felt a cold band around his chest and saw that Alberto was telling him that John, who must now be almost twenty-five years of age, was moving into another phase of his journey.

"You have had a particularly novel experience of God's

grace," reflected Alberto as he realized what was passing through Jacopone's mind. "Our Lord plunged you into deep darkness at your conversion and your periods of purgation and illumination seemed to run into one another. And so it has continued."

"Yes, my father," replied Jacopone. "But when Sebastiano flung his stinging rebuke at me on the road near Montefalco I knew that my days of individual action were over and that my will had to undergo submission to the will of God. That was the end of one phase and the beginning of another."

"And you have learned your lesson well," returned Alberto, "though it is not easy for a man of mature years. And you have still more to learn — the road winds on ahead. So then, why don't you take up this invitation from Brother Mario — though it is more than that — and make your way to La Verna?"

"I will do that very thing," said Jacopone. So for the next few days he prepared himself for the journey which he felt would yield a deep meaning both for him and for Brother John.

One September morning soon afterwards he set out from Todi on foot, determined to use the time of his travel in thought and prayer rather than in itinerant preaching.

Over the long journey he thought of the vows which were the primary instrument of his discipline at San Fortunato. He rejoiced in the first vow of poverty — but desired much greater stringency than was possible in a convent of the *mitigati* rule. Obedience was the vow which made him wince. It was not that he wished to move out of God's will for him, but ecclesial obedience did not, for Jacopone, always seem to coincide with what he believed was God's will!

And celibacy? He was not tempted with the kind of lust that had driven some friars to secret sexual encounters with certain local women who seemed to have a fascination for men under vows! And he had no preference for those of his own sex.

But there were times when he thought of Vanna — when he longed for the touch of a woman's hand, not only in physical embrace but in wifely comfort. He remembered with a smile the feeling that engulfed him when he was clothed with his new habit at his profession in vows. Margarita had made it for him and he supposed that she had "put love in every stitch" as she had when she had patched his tertiary *bizocone.*

He also remembered the day not so long ago when he had allowed himself to face up to, and admit, his feeling of deprivation because of the lack of a woman's touch. Why was it that he had been so long in honestly admitting this?

"I am certainly deprived," he acknowledged as he strode along the road. "I feel it in physical need, in emotional warmth and in a hunger of spirit that causes me an aching yearning which nothing else seems to satisfy or assuage. Yes, I am deprived. But what of it? God calls me to remain alone and He knows it is sometimes almost impossible."

There had been times as he had wandered in the hills above Todi that he had felt God offer him the way of marriage and family. And then, as if to complicate or negate the offer, the Lord would take him up in such inebriation of spirit that Jacopone would cry out in joy — rolling or dancing before the Lord for very gladness of heart, and often with tears. At such times he would cry out: "Have your own way, O Lord — for therein is my peace."

In this context he thought of John of Fermo. John had been ten years of age when he had asked to be transferred to the Order of Friars at Fallerone. He had been professed at thirteen years. There had been much discussion within the Order about years of discretion. The friars in Paris had been accused of enticing boys into the Order without their parents' consent. But John had never looked back — the threefold vow was all joy to him, and his only love seemed to be the love of Christ.

Jacopone envied him somewhat in this. To think of being so utterly given to the divine Love from a child that nothing, nothing would deflect you! To think of being so inebriated, enamoured, captivated with the crucified and risen Christ that all the world seemed but refuse and loss in compassion — this was something that stirred Jacopone's soul to its very depths.

Alas, for almost forty years he had been worldly, arrogant and superficial. His case was so far gone that only tragic bereavement and distraught madness had been able to rescue him. But now he was, as Alberto had said, a twice-born soul!

He was making the long journey from San Damiano to La Verna. But this time Brother John was to be there.

Jacopone made his way through the province of Tuscany. September was giving way to October and as he began the ascent of the mountain he was caught and chilled by a thick veil of mist that engulfed him. He had left Todi just a week before, warmed by the beauty of the September sun, and now so soon he was being drawn into mist and darkness. Was this a presage of the spiritual land of unknowing and emptiness of which Alberto had spoken? As these thoughts came to him he felt the first large drops of rain that quickly became a torrential downpour.

He struggled up through the limestone rocks between the fir trees streaming with water, and as the heavy rain gave way to a gentle drizzle and the mists parted, giving ragged views of landscape around, above and below him, he made his way past the silvery birches that seemed to shine through the mist. He was not met by a friar on this occasion but found his own way to the series of huts and hermitages which were dotted around near the summit of the mountain.

Soon he was spotted, recognized and embraced by one of the La Verna friars and found himself stripped, dried and reclothed in a ragged but dry habit, with a bowl of broth in front of a fire of logs. Brother John was not to be seen, but as soon as he had finished his broth and was warmed within and without Jacopone was taken to see the Guardian.

Brother Mario opened his arms as he had evidently opened his heart to Jacopone. "My dear brother — it has been such a long time — but now you have returned."

Jacopone felt the warmth and fervour of Mario's embrace and realized that for him it was not simply the welcoming of the former tertiary who had become a brother but the taking up of the threads of a story which had begun with Jacopone's visit twelve years previously.

Brother John had then been a name which Jacopone had mentioned to Mario and of which Mario had only learned in a dream. But now that same name was the centre around which this visit was to revolve. Brother Leo had been right, for even when John of Fermo was eleven years of age, Leo, like Simeon of old, could make his prophecy of the vision to be carried on, the experience to be entered into, the pain to be suffered and the glory to be embraced.

So Jacopone spoke his name. "May I see Brother John?"

Brother Mario broke the embrace and took hold of Jacopone by the shoulders, holding him at arm's length and looking into his eyes. "Yes you may. But first I must speak with you. Are you warmed, fed and do you need to rest?"

"I am both warmed and fed and I cannot rest until I know the situation."

So Mario sat down with Jacopone and began the story. He told him what Bruno had already recounted on his visit to Todi and then took up the story from Bruno's return.

"You know, Jacopone, that we warned you that the state of ecstasy and spiritual inebriation would not last. Indeed, it lasted three years so that we became used to Brother John, inflamed with the divine Love, crying and running through the woods and around the top of this holy mountain. He would spend many hours in tears of joy and yearning at the holy shrine of the stigmata. The whole company of friars here profited by the fervour and love of such a young man for God.

"Of course, it was also a burden. The friars here are no novices in the spiritual life and we all knew that this was that part of the mystical life which is called illuminative, and that between that and the deeper reaches of prayer called the unitive life there stretches a dark night of the soul. John's spirit was sensitive and vulnerable and his body was mortal, and we were all aware of the cost of loving God utterly. Sooner or later he would lose the glory, the exhilaration, the felt ecstasy and fire of love, and begin the path of purgation and darkness."

Jacopone felt a cold shiver pass through his whole body as Mario continued. "So it was, some months ago, that it became clear to us that God was withdrawing the sense of His loving presence from John, and though I had prepared him in mind for such withdrawal, and he had believed me and in a certain sense prepared himself, yet when it began to happen he found himself as a vessel emptied of joy and glory, and tears of sorrow and grief took the place of the cries of love.

"He attends mass diligently, comes to the required liturgical prayers, but with permission he spends long periods in silence and solitude. Whereas previously he ran from place to place crying joyfully, now he runs to those once sweet places weeping for the absence of his beloved."

"Can this be right?" murmured Jacopone sadly. "Do you not lead him back to the place of love and sweetness, my father? For you are his guide and counsellor."

"Stop now, Jacopone, and look into your own soul," replied Mario. "You know well enough that when our Lord had been baptized in the river Jordan and the Holy Spirit had come upon Him in great power and anointing he was then both led and driven by the same Spirit into the wilderness."

"I'm sorry," replied Jacopone immediately. "I know that one must go through the dark night of purgation and aridity to reach further illumination and union with God in love. Perhaps mine, like yours, is a fatherly concern for one so young. Can he bear it in body and spirit?"

"As for that," replied Mario, "he has a strong constitution, and though you will find him thin and gaunt you will perceive an inner strength of will and purpose that will bear him through this time of darkness. I believe — and hear me carefully, my brother — that the divine Spirit has brought you here to minister to John that which I cannot. And here, during this period, be it weeks or months, you will discover mutual help and comfort for the time which is to come."

Saying these words, Mario stood and placed his hands on the head of the kneeling Jacopone, praying for the grace and discernment of the Spirit of God. Then he said, "I have asked Brother John to be present at the morning mass tomorrow. Then perhaps you would both take some food — I lay that upon you under obedience — and spend as much time together as is necessary. Then I ask you to return to me singly and together to open up what the Lord has shown you."

Jacopone had felt what he called a ghostly strength enter him as he knelt before Mario for the blessing, but now he felt the fear and apprehension of his task and his unworthiness and inability to fulfil it.

"My brother," said Mario reading his face, "all that is needful will be given you. You are not alone but fulfilling the sacred trust laid upon you by Brother Leo. And he received it from Francis, who gazed upon the glory of the Crucified One."

With these words ringing in his ears and heart Jacopone went to his hut to rest.

As the sacristan lit the candles in the wooden chapel of La Verna early next morning the figure of Jacopone could be seen kneeling motionless in his place in choir. He was sensitive to the spirit of prayer which pervaded the holy mountain, now made poignant by the knowledge that Brother John had crossed over into the terrain of emptiness and aridity that Jacopone knew must be his Gethsemane.

He did not look around when Brother Mario entered to sing mass, but when the chalice and host were elevated at the altar the light reflected upon the sacred vessels caused Jacopone to glance along the choir, and suddenly he saw him.

Brother John was kneeling upright in choir. His once round and ruddy countenance was gaunt and pale. It was not a grimly ascetic image but it was one which caused Jacopone to catch his breath. And for the rest of the mass he was aware of that kneeling figure.

Soon the mass was over and Jacopone made his way alone to the hut indicated to him the night before by Brother Mario.

There was no-one else there when he entered, but a simple breakfast was set on the low table and two stools awaited the friars in the light of the flickering candle — though the morning was growing lighter by the minute.

Suddenly John appeared — four years older, thinner and ascetic and with a difference of mien that Jacopone could not at first understand. They stood gazing at one another for a moment, and then slowly but deliberately walked toward one another. Jacopone suddenly took John in a fatherly embrace and looked at his face. John was weeping.

All Jacopone's defences crumbled and they said nothing but wept together upon one another's shoulders.

Eventually Jacopone said, "I think Brother Mario put us under obedience to eat breakfast." And realizing Mario's canny wisdom they sat, ate and drank, though very little, and thus they were able to weave together the pattern of each other's experiences.

It was quite clear to Jacopone that John was a lover who had lost his beloved — and he sighed inwardly as he recognized how alike were the symptoms of the divine and earthly loves.

"What I have been unable to understand, Jacopone," said John quietly, "is that Brother Mario told me quite clearly that my time of intense joy and inebriation could not last and that it would give way to the experience which engulfs me now.

"The reality is something far and away more devastating and desolate than anything I had imagined. It was not as if I had not tried to prepare myself — yet I was utterly unprepared for this."

"Do you then recognize that this is a genuine part of the journey?" asked Jacopone. "Can you feel that this period is as much the will of God as what went before, and that this is an indispensable part of the way to the mystery of Love?"

"I *believe* it, Jacopone, but I cannot *feel* it," replied John with anguish on his face. "How can it be that such ecstasy can give way to such desolation? I have no sense of God's love, let alone His presence. I wish that I could feel His judgement but I feel nothing . . . and it is hard to bear . . ."

Jacopone was afraid of saying the wrong thing, but he remembered Mario's words about being given what was needful and so he said, "My dear brother, we have known one another since your visit to Todi four years ago, but we were together for only two weeks then. And yet I feel closer to you than to anyone on earth."

"And I, too," replied John with tears in his eyes.

"Well then," continued Jacopone, "I want to tell you my story. During our two weeks we talked of *jubilus*, of joy and ecstasy in believing, in sharing and communicating the love and light and glory of the Crucified and Risen One. But I did not tell you of my pain and loneliness, of my madness and burden. But I would tell you now."

So as John listened Jacopone related to him the story of his bereavement, his conversion, his madness and his love. He unburdened his whole heart to John, and John listened and received it all into himself.

When Jacopone finished he felt what seemed to him the flow of healing and absolution from the hands of Brother John who was holding him — Jacopone's face against John's chest.

"What is this?" cried Jacopone. "I am the one who sought to bring you healing, and you pour healing into me."

"Perhaps that is the way it must be," said John. "Only those hands can heal which are pierced. But you have also spoken to my condition, and my loneliness and desolation has mingled with yours, and compassion has been born of our mutual suffering."

This was a revelation to them both and now it was John's turn to tell Jacopone of how, in anguish of heart, when God had withdrawn from him all delight and radiance, after three full years of ecstasy, he had run and shouted, cried and wept in desolate anguish and pain.

This desolation continued for many months with no help or relief save the assurance from Brother Mario that he should endure it all with a certain passivity of spirit, for the sake of the Beloved, and all would ultimately be well.

Then John looked fully and lovingly into Jacopone's face and said, "This morning is the only experience of help and comfort I have had in all these months."

"And what do you think you have learned?" asked Jacopone.

"I think I am learning," replied John slowly, "that if God's will is for me to be without joy or consolation, and for the sake of love to be empty and alone, then I shall embrace it with trust and joy in my emptiness."

Jacopone nodded slowly. "Yes," he replied. "I believe that this is the beginning of sorrows for us both. But if we can together understand that it is also the way of love, then we shall never again believe that we are utterly forsaken — in spite of what we feel."

"We are so utterly different and yet so much the same," murmured John. And as they compared the pattern of their lives through the morning and walked together through the October sunshine of the mountain in the next few days they felt the pattern emerging of which they were a part.

They went singly and together to Brother Mario, and the objectivity and wisdom of his comments and counsel only underlined their own conclusions — and the days lengthened into weeks.

Jacopone had been reading in the book of Exodus at the beginning of November, and like the children of Israel he had sought the guidance of a cloud by day or a pillar of fire by night to tell him when he was to strike camp and move on his way.

His intuition was not wrong in this, for something very beautiful happened to John which gave them both permission to separate with immense joy and hope.

John had been particularly heavy of heart one day as he walked through the woods of La Verna alone. He had been weeping and burdened for his love and sat down beneath a beech tree, lifting up his tear-stained face to heaven.

Jacopone came upon him in this situation but did not speak or go near, for John was unaware of his presence. Then the strange thing happened.

John suddenly looked a little to his left and his eyes opened wide, his whole body began to tremble and he threw himself down on the grass beneath the tree.

"Help me, O my Lord!" he cried. "Without You, my most dear Saviour, I am in darkness and mourning; without You, O most gentle Lamb of God, I am in anguish and in pain and fear; without You, O Son of God, I remain in shame and confusion. Give me light for my blindness, bread for my hunger, life for my dying, O my most beloved Jesus . . ." and with a torrent of crying and longing he wept and moaned.

Jacopone wanted to turn and run, for it was as if he had broken in upon two lovers. But just then John stood up and took to his heels, following after what obviously was to him a vision of the Christ.

Three times he repeated such cries of yearning and desolation, and the third time a wonderful transformation took place.

First of all he knelt weeping and said, "I bathe Your sacred feet with my tears, O Lord, and kiss them for very love."

And then he knelt upright and said, "I hold and kiss Your sacred hands, my Lord, pierced for my sinning."

And then he stood upright and bowed his head, opening wide his arms, saying, "I lay my head upon Your merciful breast, O Lord; by Your most holy passion and by the power of Your precious blood shed for me, revive my soul in the grace of Your love . . ."

Jacopone was not only held in the wonder of it all but he was assailed by a mysterious and divine fragrance which seemed to unite all the sweetest odours of the world.

John stood upright again with open arms and although the October sun had disappeared he was surrounded by a shining radiance which enveloped and enamoured him, as he cried out, "O Sacred Heart of Jesus, shine on me; transform me in Your love; unite me in Your passion . . . my Lord and my God!"

He then fell to the ground in a swoon and Jacopone ran to help him. He saw nothing save the radiance illuminating the area around the path, but the fragrance which had wafted to him from a distance now enveloped both John and himself, and he fell to prayer and silence.

This marked the end of John's aridity and desolation, and proved to be the sign for their parting. Jacopone encouraged John to make a written account of his former ecstasies, his months of desolation and the experience of his vision of the risen Christ. For as he told Jacopone afterwards, he had seen the risen Jesus at his left in the glade, and what Jacopone had imagined from John's words were presented to John in vision.

"But I shall have to write plainly," teased John with a shy smile, "for I cannot rhyme like an educated man."

Jacopone chuckled at John's gentle humour, and after a profound and intense time of prayer and sharing together he wrote for them both a dialogue which spoke of the glory and the pain of the cross of Christ. He made two fair copies and in a simple act of covenanted trust and fidelity to one another in Christ, they exchanged the copies and kept them close as tokens of love. The poem read:

Contemplation of the Cross
A dialogue Between Two Brothers

I flee the Cross that does my heart devour,
I cannot bear its ardour and its power.

I cannot bear this great and dreadful heat;
Far from the Cross, from Love, on flying feet
I haste away; my heart at every beat
    Consumes me with that burning memory.

        Brother, why do you flee from this delight?
        This is the joy I yearn for, day and night.
        Brother, this is but weakness in my sight.
            To flee from joy and peace so cravenly.

121

Brother, I flee, for I am wounded sore,
My heart is pierced and sundered to the core;
You have not felt the anguish that I bore,
   Else you would speak in other words to me.

      Brother, I find the Cross all garlanded,
      And with its blossoms do I wreathe my head;
      It wounds me not — no, I am comforted;
         The Cross is all delight and joy to me.

I find it full of arrows sharp, that dart
Forth from its side: they reach, they pierce my heart!
The Archer aims His shafts that tear and smart;
   And through my armour He has wounded me.

      I once was blind, but now I see the light;
      Gazing upon the Cross I found my sight.
      Beneath the Cross my soul is glad and bright;
         Far from the Cross I am in misery.

Not so with me: this Light has made be blind!
So fierce the lustre that around me shined,
My head is giddy and confused my mind,
   My eyes are dazzled that I cannot see.

      Now can I speak, I that was once so dumb;
      'Tis from the Cross that all my powers come;
      Yes, by that Cross, of Thought and Love the Sum,
         Now I can preach to men full potently.

The Cross has made me dumb, who once spoke well;
In such a deep abyss my heart does dwell,
I cannot speak, and nothing can I tell;
   And none can understand or talk with me.

      Lo, I was dead, and now new life is mine,
      Life that was given me by the Cross divine:
      Yes, parted from the Cross, in death I pine,
         Its presence gives me all vitality.

I am not dead, but dying day by day;
Would God that I were dead and passed away!
Eternally I struggle, gasp and pray —
    And nothing that I do can set me free.

        Brother, to me the Cross is all delight;
        Beneath it dwells no torment nor affright:
        Perhaps you have not felt that Union's might,
            Nor that Embrace that clasps so tenderly?

Ah, you are warmed; but I am in the Fire:
Yours the delight, but mine the flaming Pyre;
I cannot breathe within this furnace dire,
    Or bear the flame of Love's intensity.

        Brother, your words I cannot understand:
        Why do you flee from gentle Love's demand?
        Tell me your state, and let me take your hand,
            And let me listen to this mystery.

Brother, you breathe the perfume of the Wine;
But I have drunk It, and no strength of mine
Can bear the onslaught of such Love divine,
    That Lover ceases not to rapture me.

And with that parchment stitched next to his heart Jacopone
returned to Todi.

10   Hermit Pope

The evening sun was setting over Todi in the year 1294 as the friars of San Fortunato convent sung and chanted Evening Prayer. When the Office had finished the brothers went to their cells for meditation and everything was still.

Brother Guilio, who was one of the *zelanti* friars and therefore not welcome at the Conventual convent in Todi, crept up to the little-used external door beneath the cell of Brother Jacopone. He listened intently outside the cell, then without knocking cautiously opened the door. The last rays of the evening sun slanted across the prostrate form of Jacopone stretched out on the floor in the form of a cross.

Guilio slipped in, closing the door. He tried to control his breathlessness and excitement. "Jacopone," he rasped in a hoarse whisper, "get up and listen to me. We have a pope — and it is Pietro da Morrone!" He put his foot beneath Jacopone's shoulder and turned him over.

"Is that door closed, you fool?" retorted Jacopone, irritated by Guilio's rude entry disturbing his meditation. "Pietro da Morrone is pope — and you think the Kingdom of God has come!"

"Well, yes," cried Guilio. "Or almost! How else would the hardened hearts of those scheming cardinals he moved — and why are you not dancing, laughing, weeping for joy?"

Jacopone got to his feet, took hold of Guilio by the shoulders of his rough habit and set him down upon the pallet in the corner of the cell. "The Kingdom of God does not come so easily, my friend," he said with a wry smile, "and Lucifer the fallen can appear as an angel of light."

Guilio scrambled to his feet. "What are you saying, Jacopo?

Don't you know that the cardinals have been trembling in their shoes becasue they have heard the voice of God? The election of the holy hermit Pietro was in response to an apocalyptic warning from God. The prophecies of Joachim of Fiore are coming to pass before our very eyes, and the new age of the Holy Spirit begins to dawn as I speak to you. Our Franciscan *zelanti* brothers are as excited as I am. And so should you be!"

Jacopone had already seen the papal messenger's report, which filled out his own knowledge of the situation. He turned to the *zelanti* friar: "Don't be so hasty with your predictions, Guilio. Listen to what happened and then think again. A few days ago the eight remaining cardinals who have been intriguing and quarrelling for two years since the death of Pope Nicholas received a letter via Cardinal Latino Malabranca. It went like this:

> Thus says the Lord God: Ho, shepherds of Israel who have been feeding yourselves. Should not shepherds feed the sheep? You eat the fat, you clothe yourselves with the wool, you slaughter the fatlings; but you do not feed the sheep. The weak you have not strengthened, the sick you have not healed, the crippled you have not bound up, the strayed you have not brought back, the lost you have not sought, and with force and harshness you have ruled them. So they were scattered, because there was no shepherd; and they became food for all the wild beasts. My sheep were scattered, they wandered over all the mountains with none to search or seek for them."

Guilio gaped at Jacopone with open mouth as he quoted the very words of Ezekiel the prophet which had been contained in the letter read out to the cardinals. As Jacopone declaimed the words with flashing eyes, Guilio shivered, and felt that this day he was in the midst of the prophetic signs and wonders foretold within the spiritual party of the Franciscan friars since the days of the holy Abbot Joachim of Fiore, who had died at the beginning of the century. And Jacopone continued, as if he

were the prophet Ezekiel denouncing apostate Israel and
pronouncing judgement upon the false shepherds:

> Now hear me, false shepherds, for I am against you, says the
> Lord. Bloated with your own indifference, lining your own
> purses and stirred up with internal factions, you have
> neglected my sheep. If you do not stir yourselves from your
> lethargy and give your hands to the task I have set you, my
> vengeance will be visited upon you, and you shall be removed
> from your places.
>
> Repent, then, pray and seek my face. Seek to know the
> shepherd of my choice, and cause him to sit in the holy place.
> Then shall my sheep be led out of darkness and shadow and
> into the verdant pastures of my choosing, says the Lord, the
> great Shepherd of the flock.

Jacopone stopped suddenly, took a deep breath, and sat down
trembling upon the stool beneath the crucifix in his cell. Guilio
stared at him incredulously. "Did *you* have a hand in that letter,
Jacopone?" he asked. "Letter there was, judgement was
threatened if the cardinals failed yet again. But the letter was
said to have come from Pietro da Morrone himself, from his
hermitage in the Abruzzi. And so scared were the cardinals that
the cry went up: 'Pietro Morrone for pope!' and the cry was
answered by his election."

Jacopone's breathing became regular again, and his grip
upon the three knots in his monastic rope relaxed. "No, I had no
direct hand in the letter," he replied, "but Pietro and I have long
talked about the need for a prophetic word to the Roman curia.
I left him some time ago poring over the prophecy of Ezekiel,
and it seems that the Lord has inspired and stirred up his spirit
to address the cardinals. I am afraid, though, that the result it
has accomplished is the last thing that Pietro expected, and I
fear for it. He is a cunning prophet but a poor politician."

The sun had disappeared by now and Jacopone lit the single
candle upon his table. Guilio noticed that his hand was shaking
as the flame caused shadows to dance upon the bare walls. "But

think what a glory it will be," he responded with wide eyes. "A holy man, a man of prayer upon the throne of Peter. His whole life has been one of saintliness and contemplation — and he has now shown himself to be a prophet of God . . ."

"Ah yes," interrupted Jacopone, "but is it saintliness and contemplation that the cardinals want? And prophets frequently find themselves at the point of a sword. I wonder if Benedetto Gaetani, the Orsini cardinal, plans to manipulate the saint for his own ends. Poor Pietro gave up the government of his hermit Order over a year ago. He's nearly eighty years old now, and has been in his solitary hermitage on Morrone ever since. He wanted to end his days there."

Guilio reflected on this, and his excitement cooled. "But surely, Jacopone, if God calls him to the seat of Peter he cannot refuse. And if he is elevated pope, think what good will come of it."

"Yes," reflected Jacopone, "*if* God calls him. And if not — what harm will come of it!"

"Do you not then believe this to be God's will?" cried Guilio, his excitement rising again. "Surely this is what we have been waiting for. The *zelanti* brothers of our Order have prayed and longed for this very thing. You yourself have railed against the curruptions of the Church and the evils of its curia. This surely is the beginning of the age of the Holy Spirit in which, as Joachim the Abbot prophesied, saintliness will replace corruption and the saints of God shall reign upon the earth."

Jacopone flinched. "Be careful with your interpretation of Joachim's prophecies, dear brother. There is a political edge to them which Joachim did not envisage, and the Orsini faction of cardinals will not be pleased to hear such heresy. Benedetto Gaetani will hear those words as a rallying call from the Colonna faction."

Guilio's face fell. "But you know me, Jacopone. I have no time for worldly politics, and no faith in them. I long for righteousness, truth and love; for justice, equality and reconciliation."

"That's how it all begins," murmured Jacopone. "But when such spiritual qualities are translated into concrete realities, it means that the high and mighty are pulled down from their seats. And that means political conflict, for someone has to pull them down, and then follows the reign of the saints — or their persecution to the death! No, no my dear brother. I *do* rejoice at the election. I can believe it to be God's will in spite of the cardinals, but I do forsee trouble ahead, and I hope poor Pietro da Morrone is strong enough to bear it."

Jacopone took hold of the end of Guilio's ragged and fraying rope, pulling him over to the stool, and setting him upon it. He then took his Latin New Testament and opened it at the first letter of St Peter. They were silent for a while and then Jacopone began to read: "*Pascite qui in vobis est gregem Dei . . .*"

Tend that flock of God whose shepherds you are, and do it, not under compulsion, but of your own free will, as God would have it; not for gain but out of sheer devotion; not tyrannizing over those who are allotted to your care, but setting an example to the flock. And then, when the Chief Shepherd appears, you will receive for your own the unfading crown of glory . . .

Silence. The candle flickered, and the two friars, one seated and one standing were motionless. Then Guilio stirred, rose to his feet, and they held one another in brotherly embrace for a few moments. Guilio took his leave of Jacopone more subdued then he had come, slipping out of the lower door quietly, and making his way into the growing shadows of the town.

Jacopone knelt on the bare floor of his cell with a sigh, and looked up at the crucifix on the wall. "O crucified Jesus," he whispered, "You preached and lived those very qualities that Guilio has enumerated, and look where it led You! Perhaps that is Pietro's path, the path of the spiritual sons of Francis, and therefore my path too. Grant me light to know, and strength to do Your will."

He then prostrated himself on the floor of his cell, opening heart and mind to the will of God.

Pietro da Morrone trembled in his cell high in the Abruzzi above Rome. It had been immensely difficult to surrender his role as founder and leader of his monks. He had been a monk from the age of seventeen, and solitude had called to him from the beginning. He remembered the days of extreme cold when he was twenty years of age, in the January of 1235, living in a cave in the mountians of the Abruzzi, and the extreme sexual temptations which attacked him yet did not deflect him from his monastic quest. Those were days of poverty, simplicity and immense joy before his ordination as a priest.

The pride and splendour of Rome had filled him with dismay after he was persuaded to be ordained, and by 1240 he was back among the mountains and woods of Morrone. Others joined him and hermit cells multiplied. The monks tilled the land, and when at last Pietro yearned for solitude again, he left the others, ascending further up to a wilder place at the top of Mount Majella.

The fame of his austerities and saintliness followed him, and his practical abilities and his way of dealing with his fellows brought about the building of the monastery of San Spirito in Majella under the rule of St Benedict. His foundation produced an Order of sanctity and austerity, coarse habits and plain food, with exposure to the wild weather of the mountains.

This monastery, together with others under his care, and his Order of Hermits, had their roots firmly planted, and his rule had been confirmed by the Council of Lyons in 1274. He was venerated as a saint throughout all Italy, and supported especially by the powerful Colonna cardinals. Jacopo Colonna and his nephew Piero were also friends and patrons of the Spiritual party of the Franciscans, so the paths of Pietro da Morrone, Jacopone da Todi and the Colonna cardinals had often crossed.

All this he had surrendered. At first he missed his monastic brethren. He missed being needed, he missed the quiet pattern of many minds and hearts moving together in liturgy and work. And he missed (it had to be confessed) wielding an austere authority and applying his primitive rule.

But all that had faded, and had given way to a gentler, though austere life, a simpler and more contemplative way, and an increase in the sense of the mystery and love of God. All his youthful aspirations and early dreams of the contemplative way were coming alive again, and he was realizing how much he had forgotten through the distractions of administration and a busy monastic life. More than once he had remarked to Jacopone that organized religion can keep a monk from the love of God. And Jacopone had agreed!

Then this thing had happened! From the vantage point of his hermitage he had been tempted to shake up the slothful cardinals who were more concerned with internal political intrigue than in filling the vacant chair of Peter.

He trembled now in his stone cell, and tears fell upon his coarse and ragged habit. Suddenly he felt old and tired. The years of austerities and meagre diet had caused his bones to stick out, and if his habit had been removed his rib cage would have been clearly visible. He thought of the letter he had written, in a spirit of prophetic fervour, to the assembled cardinals in Perugia, and began to regret it.

Before his retirement as a hermit, Pietro had talked with Jacopone after the death of Pope Nicholas IV, and they had found themselves to be of one mind about the condition of the holy Roman Church. Jacopone had written his stanzas castigating the apostate priesthood and the hedonistic and arrogant bishops:

Where are the Prelates, just and vehement?
To feed their flocks their ardent lives were spent.
False pomp and ostentation now are bent
    This noble Order to attenuate.

Jacopone had gone so far as to call the Roman Curia the

Antichrist, and to talk of the dismantling of its secular administration. He and Pietro had shared dangerous and prophetic thoughts.

"These months in solitude have stirred up the spirit of prophecy which I cherished in my early days," he thought, "but I had no authority and reputation then. Now that I have dispatched my apocalyptic letter to Cardinal Latino I find myself shivering, not with prophetic fervour, but with fear."

He was not afraid of misunderstanding, or even of hatred and persecution. Indeed he would have welcomed opposition, and was well used to it in maintaining his hermit vocation and his Order of Hermits against a worldly Church. He even thrived on it! But now he began to see what had been hidden from him before he had sent his letter. How could he have been so lacking in foresight?

Only that very morning, Roberto, one of the mendicant friars belonging to the *zelanti* group, had made it his business to climb the mountain of the Morrone in the Abruzzi to tell Pietro of the announcement which had rocked Perugia and reverberated in the city of Rome: "Pietro da Morrone for pope!"

Roberto, together with the other *zelanti* brethren, had received the news ecstatically, and he quoted the words of Joachim's prophecy concerning the epoch of the Holy Spirit: "The ministers of God will lead a spiritual life, dwelling in prayer and contemplation." Then he announced Pietro's election with a shining radiance on his young face, and fell down before him in tears.

But ecstasy was not Pietro's response. Rather it was trembling. He was in his eightieth year, his energy had not abated, nor his love for God, but he was weary of the Church and of the world. He had fought his fight and almost finished his course. He had kept the faith, and now he longed to enter into the depths of the contemplative love which had haunted his days and nights from his youth. His intense and single desire was to live in the light of God's love in his simple hermitage, in solitude and prayer.

The rest of the morning had been spent in the perplexity and alternation between prayer and thoughts of flight. But where could he go, and what could he do? Had he not forseen the possibility of his own election following upon such a prophecy? He almost blamed the prophet Ezekiel for his own apocalyptic fervour. And what if God *was* calling him to occupy Peter's chair, to initiate the reign of the Spirit, to bring back purity, holiness and stability to God's Church on earth; and what if, in him, the prophecies of Abbot Joachim were to be fulfilled? Indeed, he wondered if he had known this all along, but had not admitted it.

After Roberto had left, dancing down the hill with joy and tears, Pietro gave in to the temptation to run. When he had withdrawn from the Abbey of Sulmona two years before, to go to the hermitage of St Onofrio, two miles up the mountain in a steep cleft of rock, the Sulmonese folk had surrounded him, carrying crosses, torches and banners, singing and pleading with him to stay with them. But he had adamantly turned his back on them for the sake of love, and entered into the solitude in which he sought the blessedness of the vision of God.

He did not think of his solitude as isolation, and certainly not as loneliness. It was in solitude that he felt the deepest law of his being was fulfilled, and he found himself groaning in spirit for the ills of the Church as much as he felt the stirrings of ecstatic love for God. It was that very concern and longing for the sanctification of the Church that had prompted him to write with such prophetic zeal to the assembled cardinals in Perugia, after reading the prophecy of Ezekiel concerning the false shepherds.

"But fool that I am," he murmured breathlessly as he stumbled over the stones of the mountain, "I did not realize that the judgement would rebound on my own head." Then the strap of his sandal broke, and he fell and lay there groaning and remembering the words of the psalm which he had recited in his night office a few hours previously:

He digs a pit and hollows it out;
   but falls himself into the trap he had made for others.

Before he could haul himself up, he heard noises of shouting and singing from far on his right. Lifting his head cautiously he saw in the distance a crowd of men and women, with the shrill voices of children some way behind them. Obviously, the *zelanti* friar had spread the news!

Then he heard, lifted on the breeze, the sound of his own name and the tune of one of the folksy songs of Jacopone da Todi which the penitents were accustomed to sing in their processions:

> *Wisdom 'tis, full joyfully*
> *Crazed for Jesus Christ to be!*

No such learning can be found
In Paris, nor the world around;
In his folly to abound
   Is the best philosophy.

Who by Christ is all possessed
Seems afflicted and distressed,
Yet he's Master of the best
   In science and theology.

Who for Christ is all distraught
Gives his wits, men say, for naught:
Those whom Love has never taught
   Think him foolish utterly.

He who enters this glad school
Learns a new and wondrous rule —
"Who has never been a fool
   Wisdom's scholar cannot be!"

He who enters on this dance
Enters Love's unwalled expanse;
Those who mock and look askance
   Should do penance certainly.

He who worldly praise achieves
Jesus Christ his Saviour grieves,
Who Himself, between two thieves
    On the Cross hung patiently.

He who seeks for shame and pain
Shall his heart's desire attain
All Bologna's lore were vain
    To increase his mastery.
    Wisdom 'tis, full joyfully
    Crazed for Jesus Christ to be!

Before his limbs could obey his command a thought flashed through Pietro's mind: "How ironic — if they believed those words they would leave me alone in my hermitage!" But there they were — marching, singing, stumbling, tumbling, almost dancing to greet him, to celebrate the election of their own hermit as pope. But they had not seen him yet.

"Oh, what am I to do?" he cried. "I cannot run fast or far — and where can I run to anyway?"

So he lifted himself up, removed his loose sandal and scrambled back to his hermitage, locking himself in. This small hut, which had been his heaven on earth, now became the fiery furnace of the book of Daniel. He groaned in spirit and waited in fear.

Hardly had he bolted the door when the first of the people began to arrive, surrounding the rough two-celled hermitage with its narrow frontage covered with wild flowers. He looked out of the barred opening of his window, and as soon as the people caught sight of him in his ragged, stained habit, they began to shout.

Brother Roberto's rumour had been confirmed, and hot upon the heels of the people came the papal legates from the conclave at Perugia. At the Abbey of Sulmona they had met Charles, King of Naples, with his son Charles Martel. Cardinal Piero Colonna was also with this company, and Stefaneschi the eulogist, who kept his wary eye on the whole company and missed nothing, ready to carry back a wealth of detail to his master Benedetto Gaetani.

This latter company was led by the Archbishop of Lyons, and amidst cries of "*Evviva il papa!* Long live the pope!" he prostrated himself before the hermitage window, and then cried out: "The conclave of cardinals met at Perugia on the fifth of July, 1294, have unanimously elected Pietro da Morrone as Pope."

Poor Pietro opened his door with shaking hands, and stared out bleakly at the archbishop. "I am not worthy," he cried, shaking his head, "and I am too old to serve the Church." The thought of sitting in the chair of Peter caused him to start trembling again.

"It is the will of God," shouted Cardinal Piero Colonna, and the people roared in affirmation.

"Oh, let me go and pray for guidance," cried the poor hermit, vainly playing for time.

The King of Naples, the cardinals, legates and assembled people waited . . . murmuring . . . praying . . . softly singing, with a quiet, mounting excitement and expectancy in the air, for no-one doubted the outcome.

Inside his cell Pietro felt the texture of Mount Morrone beneath his feet. His yearning for solitude grew more profound and his hope of solitude more distant. In one instant, as if in the experience of a drowning man, his whole life of longing faith, of ascetic practice, of monastic leadership, of desire for solitude, passed before his eyes.

Before him lay not solitude but isolation — the isolation of the papal chair, and behind that the strange prophetic warning of a dark prisoner's cell — and death itself. The image of John the Baptist imprisoned by Herod flashed upon his inward eye. Shuddering he returned to the present moment as the murmuring, singing and praying of the people faced him with the responsibility of obedience.

The people watched as the cell door slowly opened, and the old man emerged with tears in his eyes and consent upon his lips

— but they could not see the confusion and perplexity within his heart. A great shout went up, and the archbishop read the letter of the Conclave.

By this time more people had gathered, among them some of the *zelanti* Franciscans of Angelo of Clareno, who hailed Pietro as a hermit pope, a man of prophecy, prayer and holiness, and not a political manipulator and worldly prelate as they had been accustomed to in the past.

For them the time of the *viri spirituales*, the spiritual men, had come, and the Kingdom of God seemed imminent with Pietro's consent. This was the inauguration of the era of the Holy Spirit, prophesied by Abbot Joachim of Fiore.

A donkey was led forward. Pietro had no packing to do, no affairs to set in order, no worldly business to transact, no change of clothing to wear. He was ragged, tear-stained, bowed, bony and old. His white hair was uncombed and matted, his face pale and anxious and his beard straggly. He was set upon the donkey, with Charles Martel, King of Hungary on one side, and a cardinal on the other.

As the procession moved off, Pietro looked back at his hermitage in the pure air of the Abruzzi, and was led down away from his peace, away from the solitude, into the unknown mystery of what seemed to be the will of God. It was his to obey. And he wondered if he would ever see the place again.

The papal party stayed for some days at the Sulmona monastery, and after consultation with Charles II of Naples, whom Pietro trusted more than the cardinals, he refused to go to Perugia, pleading that he was old and used to the cold of the mountains.

"It seems to me," advised Charles, "that if you want to be away from the excessive influence of some of the cardinals, you would be wise to choose Aquila as your place of coronation."

Pietro was no fool, hermit though he was, and he knew that the Orsini faction of cardinals, especially Benedetto Gaetani, had political motives in his election which were not altogether clear.

The coronation of Pietro the hermit as Pope Celestine V, took place in front of the church of Santa Maria of Collemaggio in Aquila on 29th August, 1294. And who would have guessed, if they had not known, that the glorious Celestine was the simple Pietro, hermit of the mountains?

He had laid aside his ragged and stained habit for white and gold vestments, and with incense and fire, banners and flags, liturgy and music, some two hundred thousand people thronged the celebratory mass, from Tuscany, Apulia, the Marches, Umbria and all parts of Italy and beyond. All the eight cardinals were there, though Gaetani attended for personal and political reasons rather than spiritual ones.

Two kings led Celestine on a white horse from the monastery of Collemaggio to the Palace of Aquila, where he sat with his cardinals. Charles of Naples was the main influence upon Celestine — but Benedetto Gaetani watched and bided his time.

Jacopone returned to his cell from the community mass in the conventual friary of San Fortunato in Todi. He still sometimes felt an abrasive awkwardness with some of the brothers of the mitigated rule, for his sympathies were with the Franciscan Spirituals. He knew that some of the Conventual friars had not welcomed his admission to the Todi covenant — and there was always some tension.

Ever since the coronation mass of Pope Celestine V in Aquila, he had been dismayed and anxious. Previous to Celestine's election, he had thrown in his lot with the *zelanti* Franciscans who interpreted the rule and will of St Francis literally, "with no glosses" as Francis had commanded.

Francis had known that wolves would enter the fold as soon as he died. It had begun to happen before his death, and by 1266 there was a purging of all earlier written lives and legends of the saint, so that only the prudent and stylized work of Bonaventure should be available.

Although Jacopone had entered the convent of the mitigated

rule in 1278, he had increasingly been in sympathy with the Spirituals. He shared their desire for reform of the whole Order, their desire for poverty, holiness and a literal following of the Gospel in the light of St Francis.

He was looked up to by many tertiaries and friars in the March of Ancona as a spiritual leader, and this was often a source of embarrassment to his fellow friars in the Conventual house in Todi. But today he felt embarrassed because he seemed to be caught between the two groups.

When Celestine V was elected, a great cry went up from many of the Spiritual party — a cry of relief, of joy and hope fulfilled. Guilio, who had hurried to Jacopone at San Fortunato, and Roberto, who had struggled up to Pietro on Mount Morrone, had both personified such feelings.

Jacopone himself had felt the upsurge of hope and joy in his own heart, but he also harboured doubts about the calibre of his old friend Pietro da Morrone.

It was not his sincerity that Jacopone doubted but the physical and moral stamina of the man — and perhaps Jacopone knew too much about the political and personal in-fighting between the cardinals. He certainly believed the dark stories that were circulating about Benedetto Gaetani — and he had received well-founded information about Gaetani's schemes on Celestine.

But there were also problems with the extreme wing of the Spiritual party. Some of them were losing their spiritual and mystical sensitivities because of the political interpretations of fulfilled prophecy in Celestine's election.

Jacopone thought about the group of *zelanti* friars who were proclaiming St Francis as the Angel of the Sixth Seal of the Book of Revelation. They were already spreading stories about the collapse of the hierarchical Church system and its replacement by the *viri spirituales* — themselves of course! As Jacopone considered the problem it was emphasized by a gentle tapping upon the door of his cell.

Young Brother Roberto stood there, and Jacopone bustled

him in; he was not a welcome visitor to San Fortunato's convent because of some of the rash statements he had made in the hearing of some of the "relaxed" friars. He had said that Francis' primitive rule had equal authority with the Gospels and that no pope or council could change it.

Jacopone had rebuked him previously for his extreme opinions, but Roberto laid claim to special inner illumination by the Holy Spirit, and Jacopone understood the objections of the friars minor in San Fortunato to such a claim. Nevertheless, Jacopone and Roberto greeted one another with warmth and joy.

"It's about time I saw you again," said Jacopone affectionately. "Where have you been all these weeks? I've been relying on you to give me an eyewitness account of our hermit pope when you first broke the news to him. You were around him much of that day, were you not?"

"Was I not?" cried Roberto with great enthusiasm. "I was the one to break the news to him first of all. He was puzzling over some verses in the seventh psalm outside his hermitage in the Abruzzi when I reached him, out of breath and bursting with the news — though how he understood me I don't know because you know what I'm like when the Spirit of the Lord takes hold of me."

"Yes, I know what you are like," laughed Jacopone, "but I wonder if you need to pray for the gift of discernment to know when it is the Spirit of the Lord and when it is the spirit of Brother Roberto."

Jacopone was quite serious, but his heart was warmed and enthused by the merry countenance and youthful charisma of this brother whose love for God could not be doubted.

"Well, it was the Spirit of the Lord on that day," responded Roberto with glowing face, "for look what has come to pass since then. Of course the old man was confused. He babbled on for some minutes about the judgement of some letter he had written to Cardinal Latino — the one which started the whole thing off, and which ended up by the unanimous call: 'Pietro da

Morrone for pope!' And then he began to weep."

"As well he might," responded Jacopone, and he listened while Roberto described the whole of that day, ending with the procession entering into the monastery of Sulmona.

His brow furrowed as he listened, and he shook his head as Roberto became more and more inflamed with prophetic zeal.

"You see what is happening before our very eyes," cried out Roberto. "The two-year space while the cardinals were arguing and battling among themselves indicated the end of the reign of the Son as prophesied by Abbot Joachim, and the reign of the Holy Spirit began with the election of Celestine V.

"Brother Uberto of Casale — and you believe that he is surely an illumined man — he has reckoned that, calculating from the date of the Ascension of Christ, the year 1294 is the prophetic date and that the medicant Orders were destined to bring in this era — the Dominicans and ourselves!"

"Yes, yes I can see you have it all tied up," retorted Jacopone, "but it all sounds too neat — and your condemnation of the rest of Christendom indicates some lack of breadth and charity."

"Charity?" cried Roberto. "Why, I've heard you preach in the public square in Todi about the sins of the clergy, and I would hardly have called your sermon charitable! And your denunciations have sounded throughout the Marches of Ancona, and the whole of the province of Umbria knows that you have no love for worldly prelates. I'm hardly an extremist compared with your prophetic onslaughts!"

"Oh, you have cornered me, Roberto," sighed Jacopone ruefully, "I have always found it difficult to tread the middle way. But you know that there are still some good men among the bishops, and there are certainly good friars among the Conventuals who are offended, and even scandalized by the extremes of some of our *zelanti* brothers. I declined to join the Joachim group, for they seem to have their eye on political power. Some of the apocalyptic interpretations I have heard from them certainly did not come from the good Abbot Joachim or from Brother Leo who is said to have interpreted them."

"But our father Francis did predict apostasy in our Order," replied Roberto, "and that demonic spirits would seize power so that some brothers would have to flee to heathen countries and hide in desert places. I remember Francis' words: 'After these things I will build up the Order in its first and perfect state.' You know how Brother Angelo of Clareno and his companions were exiled to Armenia — the Antichrist arises before our eyes. It was your own poem against the Antichrist, Jacopo, which strengthened my faith in the apocalyptic visions of Joachim. You say in it that Christ is the sun, but that apocalyptic darkness threatens the world — I can repeat it by heart:

Christ the Sun, set to shine in the heavens
Is darkened, and shines not on His servants;
The Church the moon, once illuming the night,
Guided by good popes, cardinals and ministers of God
Is now black with heresy, immortality and spiritual
    darkness.
Lord God, who then can be saved?
The religious Orders, the stars, have fallen out of heaven,
For the ancient serpent the devil has broken out of
    captivity,
And the world follows his path to evil, and tribulation
    engulfs us."

Jacopone was startled by Roberto quoting from his own writings. His eyes flashed as he turned on him.

"Ah yes, Brother Roberto," he countered. "But do you remember the end of the poem? I identify three groups marked by the ancient serpent, and they remind me too clearly of some of our own groups of *zelanti* friars. Mark them well and take care that you be not found among them!

"First there are those who look for a political kingdom of Christ, and are ready to rout and slaughter even in His name. The second group pretend to prophetic knowledge, saying nothing of their own sins but condemning all who do not belong

141

to their party. The third group ache to perform miracles and signs, to conjure with the power of healing, to speak in tongues and prophesy — but lacking in human compassion they live and breathe the ethereal vapours of what they call *pure* spirituality. Beware, Roberto, that you be not too hasty to interpret prophecy and to place yourself in the vanguard of God's elect."

Roberto was silent and looked crestfallen. He was hurt in his sensitive spirit by the rebuke from Jacopone, especially because he had not been expecting such a response to his visit.

"You know I have always looked to you, Jacopone," he ventured. "Do you not see in Celestine's election the hope which has stirred us for many years? And have you not had many conversations with Pietro da Morrone in his hermitage about these very things?"

"Yes, my dear brother," replied Jacopone, relenting somewhat. "I'm sorry I am a little abrasive today, but I have been praying and reflecting over these matters, and I am afraid for poor Pietro. You remember the last Pope Celestine — some fifty years ago? He reigned for only fifteen days — and I am fearful as to how long Celestine V will last."

"But if he is God's choice, will not God give him power over all his enemies?" asked Roberto, "Will he not smite his enemies with the breath of his mouth?"

"Roberto" laughed Jacopone. "You even *sound* like an apocalyptic prophet. I *must* laugh, for I shall lose my mind if I lose my humour. You interrupted me in a poem I am writing to our dear Celestine V. I believe that his election may well be a miracle wrought by God for the good of His holy Church. But I also believe that it will take all the energy, courage, strength and faith of us all to support him in prayer and works — that he may not fail.

"The enemies of God have overcome God's servants many times in days gone by, and if we divide the Church of God by our schismatic interpretations instead of living by prayer, holiness and love, then we may become the enemies of God."

"But is it true," asked Roberto, "that you and Conrad of

Offida are going with Angelo and some other *zelanti* friars to seek Pope Celestine's spiritual protection for all of us who wish to observe father Francis' primitive rule in all its rigour?"

"Yes," replied Jacopone. "We are meeting together first, and hope to present our petition to Celestine, and at the same time I hope to present to him privately my own counsel for his pontificate — God knows we have shared much of its content in the past."

Roberto rose and went to Jacopone, putting his head lightly on the older man's shoulder. "Well, may the Lord guide you, my dear father, and may He give us all discernment to stray neither to the right nor to the left, but to follow in the way of His Spirit."

"Well said, Roberto," smiled Jacopone, giving him a brief but firm hug. "That is what I have been saying in the face of your apocalyptic judgements."

Then, cautiously opening the door and slipping into the dark passageway outside, Roberto took his leave.

Jacopone knew of the dangers besetting such charismatic friars as Roberto — dangers of excessive spirituality on the one hand, and of "bringing in the Kingdom" by political manipulation on the other.

He thought of the purity and strength shown by Pietro da Morrone as a monastic leader and a man of contemplative prayer in his hermitage. But what now that he was surrounded by scheming cardinals and prelates of the ecclesiastical world? Could he maintain a gentle but firm pontifical authority, ruling in love? Could he even survive and keep his life intact?

Jacopone prostrated himself again on the bare floor of his cell before the crucifix, and lay there motionless for a full hour. Then he rose, took up his goose quill, and wrote.

At the appointed hour he responded to the bell and sang Compline with the other friars in the chapel. He then returned to his cell and after some time of meditation he lay upon his pallet and slept.

The manuscript upon his bare table was headed: "Epistle to Pope Celestine, formerly called Pietro da Morrone".

11   Antichrist Pope

Jacopone was confused. He was a spiritual man, but of late he was being drawn more and more into the political complications that surrounded him on every side. It was not easy!

Since Cardinal Bentivenga, a native of Todi, had enlisted Jacopone as his secretary and taken him to Rome for sometimes months of absence from his convent, his links with the more prayerful of the Spiritual Franciscans had lessened. He had also been drawn more closely into political life — a necessary part of the task which the cardinal had given him, and to which he had been assigned under obedience.

When he thought of Brother John and La Verna he sighed and dismissed the thought quickly — it made him uncomfortable. The intrigues and corruption encountered in Rome were distasteful to him, and he often used his gift of sharp sarcasm against the perpetrators of injustice and bribery. So after each period of work for Cardinal Bentivenga (who himself was a moderate and good man), he returned to Todi with a deep sense of relief — until the next time.

But even in Todi he was being drawn into ecclesiastical politics. He had greeted the news of Pietro da Morrone's election to the papal chair with apprehension and had cautioned both of the *zelanti* friars, Guilio and Roberto, about their iconoclastic and Joachimite views. Such views had political overtones and seethed with dissatisfaction with the worldliness of Church and curia.

Jacopone had resisted the temptation to go the way of the harsh and pietistic *zelanti* friars who lived in filthy hovels and flagellated their bodies. Then there was the fanaticism of other friars who raged and rolled in charisms and ecstasies which they attributed to the Holy Spirit. Jacopone suspected that their visions were produced by excessive fasts and deprivation. He did concur with those friars who supported righteousness and the overthrow of evil — it was their political methods that caused him great unease.

There were contradictions within himself about all this — he felt the natural chasm that seemed to separate him from Francis and from Jesus. In matters large and small Francis had displayed a humility that came hard to Jacopone. He remembered the story of the donkey owner who, with crude and brutal behaviour, forced his animal into the friars' hut at Rivo Torto. "Get in, get in," he shouted to the donkey, but was obviously shouting to the friars to "Get out, get out." Resistance did not occur to holy Francis. "In truth, my brothers," he had said, "the vocation which God has given us is not to entertain asses, but to pray and teach men the way of salvation." And they quit the hut.

Jacopone smiled as he reflected that the consequence of that action was that the brothers were given the Portiuncula to dwell in. "But I would not have quit the hut," mused Jacopone. "I would have beaten the donkey and faced the owner with righteous indignation — and probably beaten him too into the bargain."

In a weightier matter, when Francis was faced with the arrogant and manipulating behaviour of Elias who sought control of the Order and was undermining the vision and will of Francis, he simply resigned any power or control he might have commanded, feeling it to be an obedience to the higher power of Jesus who in all His life had enjoined forgiveness and humility.

Jacopone had never worked out what he felt must be a paradox, but what to him appeared to amount to contradiction — that God in Old Testament days not only allowed, but commanded holy wars, destruction of enemies and the obliteration of all whose hearts and minds were set against his ancient people.

And what of that apocalyptic letter which Pietro da Morrone had sent to the negligent cardinals? It had achieved its aim by threatening judgement. So why was he averse to acknowledging that the Joachimite prophecies were being fulfilled? And why should not God work out His will through political channels, and why should not the violent opponents of God have a taste of their own medicine and be violently overthrown?

In any case, no violence had been done, and Pietro da Morrone had been crowned as pope. Certainly, as Celestine V, he would look for Jacopone's support as he had when he was Pietro the hermit. And he would get it!

Often, during times of prayer back at Todi, Jacopone's mind would be buzzing with the gossip, flattery and attempted briberies that had filled his days in Rome. His first contact with the Colonna cardinals had been made there, and that was because they were supporters of the *zelanti* friars.

It was in Rome also that he had come face to face with Benedetto Gaetani again. They had known each other from their younger days in Todi, when Gaetani's uncle had been a bishop there, and by a process of bribery and string-pulling, Gaetani the avaricious Guelph ecclesiastic and Jacopone the arrogant Ghibelline lawyer had become eminent fellow citizens.

Jacopone liked him even less in Rome, for all the arts of dipolomacy and manipulation were used by him for self-aggrandizement. They were both skilled jurists, but whereas Jacopone had first renounced his skills and then baptized them into the service of preaching and writing, Gaetani had unscrupulously used his gifts to procure a cardinalate.

Jacopone realized that there was a genuine love for the arts and culture in the cardinal, but that did not spark any affection in his own soul.

He had heard, with a certain satisfaction, that at Gaetani's first mass after ordination to the priesthood, all the candles had been strangely extinguished in the church and the surrounding countryside had become enshrouded in darkness.

There was also the matter of Gaetani's attitude in the election of Pietro da Morrone to the papal chair. He did not oppose it, but then he did not wholly approve of it. Jacopone, realizing his own tendency to prejudiced opinions in Benedetto Gaetani's direction, wondered if he was still scheming behind the scenes.

None of the other cardinals would vote for Gaetani, knowing what a political opportunist he was. It was common knowledge that wherever there was information to be gleaned, Gaetani's puppet Stefaneschi was found to be nosing around on behalf of his master. So Jacopone kept his eyes and ears open.

Since establishing his base again in Todi, he had kept in touch with the *zelanti* groups, and kept himself informed as to the prophetic character of the visionaries among them.

He was most happy when in fellowship with these enthusiasts, and the constant give and take of their debates was life-blood to him, though he realized that this was feeding the "old Adam" of his unregenerate legal days.

One day he had been defending his middle way between extreme asceticism and political revolution when Conrad of Offida and Ubertino of Casale opened up the debate by presenting to Jacopone some of their conversations with Brother Leo at the Portiuncula before he died.

Both these friars were held in high esteem by the *zelanti* groups, especially because of the trust vouchsafed to them by the brothers Leo and Rufino. They did not go as far as Peter Olivi, who was a reforming friar after the pattern of the Abbot Joachim.

Olivi believed that the *zelanti* mission was to force the whole Order into the unmitigated poverty commanded by Francis, and then to overturn the corrupt curia, in fulfilment of Joachimite prophecies, putting in its place holy and zealous friars.

Conrad and Ubertino concurred with the first part of that mission, but their emphasis was mystical — outward poverty being the manifestation of an inward humility of spirit. They quoted Leo who had said that Francis wanted the brothers to be like larks — their earthly life poor and humble, clad in grey feathers and nourished on the meanest things, but their celestial life joyful, musical and free.

Jacopone admired Conrad despite the fact that he never seemed to wash his habit. He had a disciplined and sharp intellect which appealed to Jacopone, and soaring mystical yearnings. He possessed a tranquillity which enabled him to spend extended periods in mystical prayer, or humbly to beg for food, preach in the marketplace or cook for the friars. He did not much like ecclesiastical church services, being a lover of nature, finding more solace in the woods than at the altar, and having an immediate relationship with animals, reminiscent of Francis himself.

Jacopone discovered that Conrad was planning to make his way eventually to a hermitage on La Verna — and this news stirred him more than he could express.

Both Conrad and Ubertino had talked to Jacopone concerning the fulfilment of the Joachimite prophecies in the election of Celestine V, and Ubertino said, "You know, Jacopone, that after a conversation with Brother Leo, Conrad and I worked out some dates, and it is my calculation that reckoning from the Ascension of Christ, the reign of the Son comes to an end with the election of Celestine V, and the reign of the Spirit begins."

"What exactly does that mean to you?" asked Jacopone.

"It means the overthrow of the Roman curia with all its corruption, and the reign of a spiritual curia, destined to be ushered in by the mendicant Orders as Joachim foretold. And that means the *zelanti* friars, with perhaps some of the Dominicans."

"Are you saying that we must become politicians or soldiers?" asked Jacopone.

"No, I am not," replied Ubertino quickly. "You know that I abhor violence. But I am saying that we must be prophets as well as saints, discerning the signs of the times."

Conrad broke in: "Leo told us that our father Francis prophesied of apostasy in the Order, and that demons should seize power among us, and that some brothers would flee to heathen countries and others hide in desert places. And then Francis said: 'After these things, I will build up the Order in its first and perfect state.' And you know that brothers Angelo, Clareno, Liberato and their band of *zelanti* followers were condemned, imprisoned and deprived of the sacraments for living and preaching the vision of our beloved father Francis."

"Yes," added Ubertino, "and they would have died there if our *zelanti* brother Raymond of Gaufridi had not become General. He released them and declared their only offence to be love of the Rule in its rigour and vigour, and sent them for safety on a mission to Armenia.

"They returned to Italy only last year, and our Minister General is encouraging them to appeal to our new pope Celestine for protection and confirmation of our primitive rule. They are seeking for support among us, for some of us believe that the election of our brother Pietro da Morrone is the will of God and the fulfilment of prophecy."

Jacopone was disturbed in spirit. These two men, Conrad and Ubertino, represented to him all that was best in the Order. They were moderate enthusiasts, refusing to resort to crude violence or intimidation, and with a zeal and love for God that inflamed his own heart. And yet they felt the need to become involved in ecclesiastical affairs that involved Church politics.

Suddenly, in the midst of such thoughts as these, Jacopone heard the voice of Conrad: "Will you, Jacopone, throw in your lot with us and come with Angelo and Liberato to seek Pope Celestine's affirmation of our primitive rule?"

Jacopone was a member of a *mitigati* house. He was a leader among both Spirituals and Conventuals. But he replied with only a slight hesitation: "I will."

Celestine V sat in his apartment in Aquila just ten weeks after his coronation, and read again the words which had been addressed to him by his old friend Jacopone da Todi.

He sighed, for it was easier being a prophet than a pope — he should know! He longed for his hermitage, his solitude among the mountains of the Abruzzi, and repeated again the words before him:

> *Pietro da Morroni, what will you do?*
> *You are brought to trial and judgement too.*

We shall see, perhaps, at last achieved
What within your cell you heart believed:
But if in you the world should be deceived,
   Judgement then will follow certainly.

Very high and noble is your fame,
Far and wide the folk revere your name;
If at last you soil yourself with shame,
   Strange confusion will the righteous see.

By this test your metal shall be told,
Be it copper, iron, or pure gold;
Be it wood or cloth or straw — behold!
   Now your acts shall tell us clearly.

'Tis a forge, this court, to try your mind,
In its fires pure gold shall be refined;
Nought but ashes will be left behind
   If from dross your metal is not free.

If in power you should take delight
Evil will infect you with its blight,
And a heavy curse your life shall smite,
   Losing God for bribes of luxury.

Anxious grief for you my heart did fill
When you did pronounce those words, "I will!"
Lest that yoke should damn your soul to ill,
   Laid upon your neck so heavily.

If a father's love you do not feel
Never will the world obedient kneel;
Bastard loyalty is empty and unreal,
   All unworthy of your prelacy.

For the cardinals are fallen low,
In an evil course their longings flow,
Never one this kinsman will forgo
　　To enrich his soul be perfidy.

Of the bishops too you must beware,
Great their hunger for unlawful fare,
And their thirst will drag you to despair
　　For no draught can quench its cruelty.

And beware the priests who'd have you think
Black is white, and white as black as ink;
If, unguarded, in their snares you sink,
　　You will sing your song full evilly.

"Counsel such as this is easier to give than to receive," he sighed. "Better if Jacopone had rebuked me for writing my own prophetic warnings to the cardinals. What I would give to reverse that episode now!"

As he dwelt on these thoughts the expected group of about a dozen *zelanti* friars from Umbria and Ancona were announced — Jacopone among them.

They were ushered into Celestine's presence. As he stood to receive them, they all prostrated themselves before him — some of them with tears, most of them with joy and one or two with apprehension.

"Come now, my brothers," said Celestine, "you and I are kinsmen in religion. I am surrounded by anxieties but you bring joy to my heart. If I can do for you something to increase the love of God, I shall do it."

Angelo was their spokesman. "You have heard, most holy father, that Brother Raymond of Gaufridi, our Minister General, has sent us to you. It is his will that we should ask your approval of our simple and primitive rule so that we may observe it without molestation or impediment from those who have deliberately declined from the faithful observance which our father Francis enjoined upon us."

Celestine bade the rest of the friars rise from their prostrate posture, and they sat on the benches placed against the two walls on either side of pontiff's chair.

He was dressed as Jacopone had never seen him before, in a cream-coloured robe which was in stark contrast to his former ragged, patched and dirty habit. He looked most uncomfortable wearing a jewelled ring and soft slippers, but his gaunt and weary face revealed his monastic soul which manifested not only tiredness, but compassion and understanding.

The friars relaxed and waited for his words. "It seems to me," he observed, "that the blessed Francis gave you a rule both primitive and perfect, and by its very nature impossible of performance by many. There are, I know, two large groups of friars who protest their inability to live by such a rule, and for them it has been mitigated to the bounds of possibility."

". . . to the level of laxity," murmured one of the friars.

Celestine smiled. "Yes, my brother, I concur with your judgement. And that is the reason why I put before you a two-fold solution which will, I hope, satisfy those of you who would keep the rule in its primitive purity without compromise, even pursuing it more rigorously, and those of you who would keep it yourselves, while exercising charity with others who cannot climb such heights."

As the friars listened wide-eyed, he outlined to them his plan of taking Angelo, and those who would follow him, under his direct obedience, with the name of *Poor Hermits of Pope Celestine*, affording them also the help and protection of his own Celestine Order of monks.

This caused some consternation among the brothers, for Angelo had asked for permission, not separation; and though it did not mean that the new formation would cause them to sever their relationships with the Franciscan Order or surrender their habit, it did appear to introduce a rupture in the unity of the one Order.

Peter Olivi became quite angry when Brother Conrad said

that he did not feel he could join such a group, but felt sympathetic support towards Angelo, Liberato and some others who were all in favour of the idea.

"Don't you see," he remonstrated, "that we must not get involved in even the appearance of schism. Only thus will we be able to influence the rest of the Order and be truly faithful to the vision of unity that was precious to blessed Francis."

Jacopone also felt that this was a wrong decision on the part of Celestine, though from generous motives. He listened while the pope revealed his knowledge of the persecution of the Spirituals by the Conventuals, and winced as he spoke of the laxity, corruption and arrogance of the *mitigati* parties in Bologna, Paris and elsewhere.

At that moment Jacopone was tempted to move out of the *mitigati* convent, surrender his secretarial duties, and seek to live a life of prayer, penance and poverty with the friars on mount La Verna.

While he was considering these things, the other brothers retired to the adjoining room to present a response to the pope, and Celestine broke in upon Jacopone's thoughts.

"Thank you for your poetic counsel, my old friend. You were very bold in writing such hard words to a poor old man who desires only solitude and peace."

Jacopone, overwhelmed by these words, found himself collapsing on to his knees in tears before the old hermit Pietro da Morrone. "Oh, my father, I am so insensitive and heartless!" he cried, "Why do I react with such arrogant pride and petulance? If I were elected pope I fear I would endeavour to establish the kingdom of God by force — according to my own vision. I have brought grief to your heart and increased your burdens."

Celestine had tears in his own eyes too as he enfolded Jacopone in his embrace, kneeling down with him. "No, my brother. Godly grief leads to healing, for you were not destructive in your words. Indeed, were our situations reversed, I doubtless would have written such a letter to you — tempered with less charity."

When the other friars re-entered the papal apartment they found the two of them weeping together. Rebuked and quietened, some of the friars stayed with the pope to discuss the details of Celestine's plan, while Jacopone, Conrad, Ubertino and Peter Olivi with some others left with the assurance of protection and approval of the primitive rule for themselves.

Celestine's reign did not last long. Jacopone's uneasiness proved justified as the weeks went by. Within the cardinalate, Benedetto Gaetani's influence wore down the pope, implying, suggesting, indicating that Celestine was both unworthy and incapable of such high office, and that he had made a mistake in accepting the papal chair. Thoughts of abdication were introduced into his mind, though such a thing had never happened before.

The friars who had taken the name of Celestine in order to do the will of Francis more perfectly, fell into great heaviness, while all the *zelanti* friars saw the effect of a saintly hermit set upon an ecclesiastical throne in the midst of ecclesiastical and worldly politicians, corrupted by greed, intrigue and violence.

Celestine was not stupid, for he forced the cardinals, including Gaetani, to come to Aquila. He was not impractical, for he made forty decrees in the first seventeen days of September 1294. And he was not cowardly, for he did not consult the sacred college but acted independently. Neither did he depart from his former innocence or compromise his own soul.

But he did not know what was going on around him. He could not cope with all the intrigues, did not know whom to trust, and became bewildered and undermined by the sheer weight of it all.

His command of Latin was poor and he conducted business in Italian, never answering verbally in public.

The one act of his own initiation which was put into effect within weeks of its approval was concerning the necessity of a speedy decision in any election of a new pope, with penalties for delays. He did not intend that there should be a repetition of the two years' delay which had occurred after the death of his predecessor Pope Nicholas IV.

As Celestine weakened in such surroundings, he began to hear voices — discouraging, denouncing, judgemental and frightening voices. Jacopone heard that they came from a speaking tube which terminated in Celestine's bedroom, with Benedetto Gaetani at the other end!

At last, he turned to Gaetani for counsel. "Is it possible for a pope to resign?"

"Yes," returned Gaetani with seriousness, "if the reasons are grave enough."

Gaetani also worked on Charles, King of Naples, who had been Celestine's supporter, though for his own reasons. The king and the cardinal planned together, and at last they agreed that Celestine needed rest and peace.

The consistory was convoked, and Celestine read his renunciation:

I, Pope Celestine V, moved by lawful reasons, to wit, humility, a desire for a better life and an unharmed conscience, likewise because of my weakness of body, my want of knowledge, the malignity of the people, the infirmity of my person, and that I may regain the peace of my aforetime consolation, of my own will give up the papacy, and definitely renounce the place, the dignity, the burden, and the honour, giving full and free faculty to the sacred College of Cardinals to elect and provide, in accordance with canonical law, a Pastor for the universal Church.

It was all done with great dignity, and as he removed his papal robes and symbols and put on his now clean but patched habit, even those who had not helped him, wept for him.

Jacopone suspected that his old friend would not be allowed back to the Abruzzi mountains, and foresaw that he would be imprisoned, and perhaps purposely neglected in order to hasten his death. It was not convenient that there should be a living pope (though abdicated) while another sat on Peter's chair!

Not only Pietro da Morrone's own group of monks, but the Celestine Hermits and all the *zelanti* friars were in despair. They met in groups, endeavouring to understand what had gone wrong, recalculating dates, reinterpreting prophecies, — but Jacopone, organizing groups of the Spirituals in a practical and systematic manner, looked at the situation as it was.

He put it to them like this: "I think I speak for you, my brothers. I do not believe in the abdication of a pope. I believe that though Pietro da Morrone may not have desired to be pope, he was duly elected and validly consecrated and crowned. Therefore he remains pope.

"We must watch and wait. I suspect that Benedetto Gaetani, the Orsini cardinal who once failed to get elected, will now inveigle his way into the supposed vacant chair of Peter."

The assembled friars set up a murmuring. Some of them were scandalized, some horrified, but most were not surprised — and all of them, at last, saw the way things were going.

Conrad of Offida spoke up: "My prayers and sympathies are with Pietro da Morrone. Gaetani put him under the guardianship of Angelerio, Abbot of Monte Cassino, so that it would not look like imprisonment. Angelerio was kind enough to allow Pietro to find his own way to him, but of course Pietro returned to his cell at Morrone, and I hear that Gaetani plans to capture him and imprison him on Lake Bolsena. What shall we see next?"

As the talk went on, the bonds of fellowship in sorrow were strengthened, and after common prayers, which included much singing, sighing and groaning, it was agreed to meet again, as many as could, the following month.

The meetings of *zelanti* brothers, certain tertiaries and sympathizers, continued month by month, in different places, all over Umbria, Tuscany, the Marches of Ancona and further afield.

What Jacopone prophesied came to pass. The Conclave met quickly in accordance with Celestine's decree, and in spite of the opposition of some of the Colonna cardinals, Benedetto

Gaetani, the Orsini cardinal, was elected as Pope Boniface VIII, on 23rd January 1295.

The sad story of Pietro da Marrone continued to its bitter end, and Jacopone co-ordinated a network of *zelanti* news across the whole Italian peninsula. One day, at a meeting of the *zelanti* brothers near the Carceri on Mount Subasio, he told of its bitter culmination.

There were about two hundred friars and sympathizers present, and as Jacopone stood up during the octave of Pentecost, on a beautiful May day on the verdant hillside under a wide, blue sky, with fleecy clouds scudding across the heavens, he gazed around him with sorrow and with strong pride.

All the friars became aware of the power of his searching eyes, and silence fell upon the great gathering.

He waited for a whole minute, as the strong breeze blew among the friars on the mountain, and then he lifted up his powerful voice:

"My dear brothers of Francis, lovers of Christ, children of God: I greet you with great joy and with immense sorrow. Some of our number have known persecution; some have been tortured by their own kinfolk, and since we last met some have died.

"Today, on this hillside above the sacred town of Assisi, we shall celebrate a requiem mass — not for them only, but especially for one of whom I will now tell you.

"On Sunday last, the Day of Pentecost, Pope Celestine V, our brother Pietro da Morrone, died in the unwholesome prison under the castle of Fumone, near Anagni. He died of ill treatment and neglect, guarded by soldiers.

"You all know the saying: '*Si Fummo fumet, tota Campanea tremet.*' Not only does the hill of Fumone fume today with anger and pain, but we are all caught up in its sorrow. Our Order needs to tremble beneath the judgement of God. And so does Benedetto Gaetani."

A great sighing and groaning took hold of the assembly,

mingling with the sound of the wind, and above it all, the strong voice of Jacopone carried over the heads of the *zelanti* friars.

'Gaetani, after imprisoning Pietro's lax jailer, sent Theodoric of Orvieto up to Mount Morrone to capture the fugitive, but his heart was melted by the hermit's innocence and lack of guile.

"When this news reached Gaetani he became afraid, for a robber anti-pope cannot stand when the true pope prays in his cell, innocent and guileless. He must be silenced.

"But Pietro was not stupid, and before Gaetani's envoy, Guillaume d'Estendart, could reach and secure the hermit, he took flight into the desert places of the Abruzzi where he wandered for two months.

"In the forests of Apulia one of his monks, who brought word to me, reported him as saying: 'It may be I shall rest here.' But he was recognized and soon his cell was surrounded by people singing, praying, venerating him as pope and saint.

"The brothers secreted him away one night, and for more than a month he was hidden in the San Giovanni monastery in Piano, below Mount Gargano.

"He was restless there, hearing of the determination of Gaetani to take him captive, so he set out to sea in a small boat bound for Greece. On the sea his peace returned and he rested in the love of God — but only for a short time.

"A storm descended and the boat ran aground near Viesti in Apulia, and while Pietro awaited the calming of the storm, he was discovered and captured."

Jacopone halted, out of breath, as an audible groan ascended from the crowd, though no-one spoke a word. They were caught up in the glory and the pain of the narration, feeling the darkening shadows as Jacopone moved towards the end of the story.

Quite suddenly, the wind died down, and with tears in his eyes, Jacopone continued: "Pietro was taken to Anagni, not in chains, but closely guarded. There Gaetani received him with pretended courtesy and told him of the necessity of saving him from his enemies for the good of the Church.

"The old man cried that he desired only to be alone with his God in the mountains, and that he had no desire to speak with any save his brothers.

"'Let the old man go to his cell,' responded the meeker cardinals. But Gaetani would brook no opposition.

"Pietro, the hermit of the mountains, was incarcerated in a dungeon in Fumone. He existed in the dank atmosphere of damp and decay — chained, guarded by soldiers, ill-treated and neglected.

"Two of his monks were taken ill in the rotting place, but one of them heard the words that Pietro spoke to Gaetani on his only visit to the dungeon.

"He had come to tell Pietro that he was there simply to avoid a schism in the holy Roman Church, but Pietro saw the arrogance and deceit that had eaten into the man's soul.

"He looked full into Gaetani's face and spoke quietly but courageously of the sacred office, usurped and defiled by this anti-pope, and then he said: 'You crept in like a fox, you reign like a lion, and you will die like a dog.'

"I shall remember those words and remind Gaetani of them one day. May God have mercy on him!"

Jacopone paused, to separate what he was about to say from all that had gone before. He lowered his voice, but could be heard distinctly throughout the whole crowd: "Our brother Pietro da Morrone lingered on for ten months, and Sister Death received him and freed him from all his pains last Sunday, the Day of Pentecost."

Then he cried aloud over the heads of all the people: "*Requiem aeternum dona ei, Domine.*"

And the answering cry resounded into the sky from over two hundred voices: "*Et lux perpetua luceat ei. Amen.*"

12   Insurrection and Excommunication

Jacopone awoke suddenly. A shadowy figure stooped over him, a hand across his mouth, and he felt himself being smothered. "Jacopo, Jacopo," came an urgent and loud whisper, "keep quiet — it's me, Deodato. You're making a hellish noise in your dreams and there are soldiers prowling around on the mountain . . ."

Jacopone relaxed, trembling and sweating, and realized where he was. It was a night in the summer of 1297. After laying the Longhezza Manifesto against the anti-pope Boniface VIII upon the high altar of St Peter's Church in Rome and nailing copies to the principal church doors, the three friars of the insurrectionist party had made for the hills above Tivoli. They were brothers Benedetto of Perugia, Deodato Ricci of Monte Prenastino and Jacopone himself — all signatories of the anti-papal manifesto.

Soldiers had soon appeared intent on rounding up first the Colonna cardinal brothers and their supporters, then the French prelates and the Franciscan *zelanti* trio who were party to the document.

The friars had separated themselves from the others and cut up into the hills. They found the cave which had been used by some of the *zelanti* group, which was in a place not easily discovered. They were now biding their time, waiting for an opportunity to get to the Colonna fortress at Palestrina where they would be safe from the papal guard.

Jacopone had had much time for reflection during the last few days and he wondered how he had got himself into such a fix. How often he had warned the *zelanti* friars about mixing politics with religion! How stupidly he had got himself into an incensed mood of hatred against the scheming successor to the papal chair, Boniface VIII!

The Franciscan vow of obedience to the pope had not been broken in Jacopone's view because Boniface had been elected invalidly while Celestine V, the hermit pope was still alive — though he had since perished in Boniface's prison.

"Are you all right now?" asked Deodato. "You must have been having a wild dream, for you were shouting something about La Verna and darkness."

"Wild it was, and sad," answered Jacopone, taking the water flask that Deodato handed to him. "In the dream I was lying on the open ground on top of Mount La Verna, bathing in the sweetness and love that such a holy place evokes in me. Suddenly a great shadow fell across the sun and I looked up in fear.

"An immense papal tiara began to descend from the sky upon the summit of the mount. It was the one fashioned by Boniface, with its two tiers symbolizing his pretended total jurisdiction over church and state.

"As this monstrosity descended, darkness fell upon the mountain, and I felt myself smothered under its oppressive weight, for the bands of metal were closing upon the sacred shrine of the stigmata. That's when I must have cried out."

"No worldly pope can destroy the reality of Francis' vision," murmured Benedetto. "His loving spirit is immune from such carnal violence and avaricious power."

"I know that, my brother," answered Jacopone. "It is not that shrine that I am concerned about, but the shrine of La Verna within my own soul — it has been usurped by my own violent lust for revenge. My frustration and anger over the forced abdication of the hermit pope thrust me into political action. And this has now involved the three of us in the manifesto which has reduced us to fleeing fugitives."

"But we did not see it as political so much as spiritual," argued Benedetto. "How were we to know that the Colonna cardinals would involve us in bloodshed and political retaliation?"

"We are stupid, that is the fact of the matter," retorted Jacopone. "How could I be so thick-headed as to have fallen into the trap of which I have warned so many others among our *zelanti* brethren?

"Political power depends on force of arms, and anger leads to violence. When we resort to other weapons than love and prayer we act neither as sons of Francis nor as disciples of Christ."

"Are you saying that we should go and seek Boniface's soldiers, give ourselves up and submit to him as our lord and pope?" asked Deodato incredulously.

"No, I am not saying that," cried Jacopone, whose patience was wearing thin. "Benedetto Gaetani is anti-pope and anti-Christ. But we have gone about the matter in the wrong way. Perhaps the only thing for us to do is to try to make our way to Palestrina and make clear our position in relation to the Colonna supporters. But first of all we must think — and pray!"

It was clear in Jacopone's mind that a pope could not abdicate. Such a thing had never happened before in nearly thirteen hundred years, and now it had happened under the plotting hand of Cardinal Gaetani, who used the abdication to manipulate himself into the papal chair. Celestine had died under the cruel hands of his captors and the apostolic succession was now broken.

Jacopone was not alone in such thinking. All sections of the *zelanti* friars held the same view, and so did the Celestine monks, and certain Dominicans. Politically the whole Italian peninsula was restless. Philip the Fair in France held Boniface to be anti-pope, as did Frederick III of Sicily and James II of Aragon.

The act which had caused Jacopone to move politically was initiated by the Franciscan Conventuals of his own Order, who accused the Spirituals of insurrection against the pope. Boniface's insecurity made him issue a violent decree against the Spirituals, overturning all Celestine's former decisions in their favour. Boniface also acted against the Colonna cardinals who had supported the Spirituals.

Jacopone, thus incensed, planted his feet on the road of political conflict, so that the Ghibelline lawyer that had been, and the reforming friar he now considered himself to be, found themselves in harmony against the anti-pope of the Guelph party.

In the role of reforming friar he had persuaded himself that he was the instrument of God, reversing all his former counsel to the political activists of the *zelanti* friars. He had previously reminded them that Francis preferred to receive rather than inflict wounds in spiritual warfare — but, as he now said, this was an exceptional situation!

Up to that point, his companions had consisted of the company of saintly friars among the *zelanti* and *mitigati* groups, and especially the mystics of Mount La Verna, with the very special friendship of Brother John. Now he seemed to be consorting with the Ghibilline nobles of Rome, the Colonna faction and the French prelates who supported Philip the Fair.

By this time the other two friars had settled down to sleep again on the floor of the cave. Jacopone was in no mood to sleep; covering himself with his patched habit, he reflected on the actual events of the past week.

The morning of the tenth of May had found the three *zelanti* friars signing what had become the Longhezza Manifesto, along with the Colonna faction and the five French prelates.

Longhezza was a Colonna stronghold, east of Rome on the Tivoli road, and the manifesto declared that Boniface called himself Roman Pontiff by the instigation of the devil, and was therefore not a legitimate pope. Celestine's abdication had been brought about by human ingenuity and therefore his successor's election was null and void. The sacraments, by the same token, had been profaned and the apostolic succession broken. The only remedy was that Boniface should lay aside his claims and that resort should be made to a General Council which should declare the truth, remove abuses and find a true shepherd for the Church. If Boniface should refuse this petition, continued the manifesto, the signatories would endeavour to restrain him from exercising all pastoral powers.

Jacopone remembered the journey of some twenty kilometres into Rome with the other friars and representatives of the manifesto to lay it upon the high altar at St Peter's, and the trail around the city, nailing copies to the doors of the principal churches.

Boniface was quick to act. He excommunicated the Colonna cardinals, giving them ten days to make their submission. They and their followers retreated to the Colonna fortress at Palestrina and remained there.

Jacopone, Benedetto and Deodato had escaped into the hills between Longhezza and Tivoli to consider their next move. It was from this vantage point that Jacopone was now trying to work out where he stood in all this confusion of faith and politics.

The feeling that he had compromised the true Franciscan vision perceived and inherited by Leo, Rufino and the more contemplative of the *zelanti* friars was increasing. Though he despised the time-serving laxity of the *mitigati* Conventuals, he respected the moderate path and discerning wisdom of Alberto. But he was ashamed to return to the convent at Todi.

La Verna now seemed to be a fading vision, and he saw a certain ironical fulfilment of the dream that had come too late. The joyful confidence in God and the *jubilus* of ecstatic love had given way to the militant instincts of a reforming friar that were far removed from Francis' vision of a little brother of Jesus.

The poetic fervour which had previously filled his songs of love could now be turned only into cynical verses of criticism and judgement upon hypocrisy. "Avenge the betrayal of the curia," ran the versification of his thoughts. "Let us attack it with anger, let us destroy it. For there the members of Antichrist call themselves Your Church. May that one especially who leads such an evil life be sent to hell for his sin."

At last Jacopone rose from the ground, feeling the stiffening in his joints and the sorrow in his heart. He kindled a fire and warmed himself, rubbing his aching muscles.

Then as the dawn was beginning to streak the skies above Tivoli he woke Benedetto; Deodato was already awake, watching him. The three of them performed their hasty ablutions at the small spring behind the cave, and Deodato, the priest among them, said mass, using what vessels he had in his knapsack, with some stale bread and not very fresh wine. Even as these elements were transformed by faith and sacramental action into the body and blood of Christ, they retained their stale bitterness.

After the reading of the Gospel, Jacopone broke into an extempore homily on the sweetness of Christ's body and blood become bitter in the tasting, and he began to sing one of his own songs, set to a Tuscan melody, lamenting the soul's sorrow for Christ's absence:

> *Weep, sorrowful Soul, despoiled of your Adored,*
> *Bereft of Christ, your Lover and your Lord.*

Lament and mourn, and shed full many a tear,
For you have lost your Lord, so fair, so dear;
Perhaps such bitter sighs may bring Him near,
    Back to my mourning heart disconsolate.

Deep cause is mine to mourn, and sore my cost,
Father and Lover — both my soul has lost;
Christ, gracious root and flower, Christ my Trust
    Has left me, for my sins that are so great.

O Jesus Christ, why have you left me so?
Disconsolate, beset by many a foe,
Beseiged by sins that fain would bring me low!
    I am too weak to strive against my fate.

O Jesus Christ, how can You suffer me
By such a cruel death destroyed to be?
Grant me to wound myself, and so be free,
    Quenching in Death my thirst insatiate.

O Jesus Christ, have You no other death
Less harsh, less dreadful for my failing breath?
Vain is my cry — in vain it clamoureth,
　For You have left me, and locked fast the gate.

O wretched heart, no longer bold and free,
Surrounded now with pain and misery,
Your cup's too full — present your piteous plea,
　And let your clamour be intemperate.

O eyes of mine, how can you cease to weep?
To mourn the vanished light you could not keep?
Your birthright you have lost, in darkness deep,
　— Of gazing on the Splendour Uncreate.

O ears of mine, and can you listen so
To these my sad complaints of bitter woe?
Have you forgot that Voice that lovers know
　That once did make me sing and jubilate?

O grief! O cruel pangs of memory!
Remorse devours and gnaws me steadily,
So tortured I am plunged in misery,
　While from my Saviour I am separate.

Now in no comrade's heart will I confide,
My life shall be a desert wild and wide;
Lonely I dwell, with crowds on every side;
　I've lost my Lord — and I am desolate!

The square linen corporal which Deodato carried with him was spread upon a rock outside the cave. The platter with the piece of bread and the earthenware pot which served as a chalice were set upon it. The friars risked being observed during the simple mass, and the other two shared the sadness expressed by Jacopone, though he felt the tensions more deeply than they.

　After the mass was over they heated some of the rabbit broth of the night before, dipping their stale crusts into it, and drank water from the spring. Then they looked at one another.

"I suppose we had better try to make our way to the Colonna fortress at Palestrina," said Benedetto resignedly. "If we are found in the open by Boniface's men we shall be imprisoned."

"The same applies to being found by our Conventual brothers," answered Jacopone, "and they'll throw in a recommendation for excommunication for full measure."

"It would be foolish to travel by daylight," put in Deodatus. "Let us make the most of this time together. It seems to me we need to sort out our own motives among ourselves in understanding the will of God. I have a family of friends this side of Tivoli, not far from here. I shall go and beg some food from them — it's not fair to ask them for refuge."

The other two looked sharply at him, and he said quickly: "Have no fear, they are quite safe — I shall be back within the hour. Then we can set off in twilight this evening, for Palestrina is about fifteen kilometres away, keeping off the road."

Deodatus' suggestion was adopted, and he returned an hour or so later with supplies of bread, meat and wine. The three friars had a more basic and honest discussion than ever they had had before about themselves and their relationship to one another and the *zelanti* party. The three of them realized that their impatience and impetuosity had caused them to throw in their lot with those whose motives were even more mixed than their own — and who were not averse to violence. And more devastating than all this — they had deviated from the way of Francis, and of Jesus.

"I must follow this path to its end," murmured Jacopone. "But I wish that I could see more clearly where the lines should be drawn. When our Lord said: 'Render to Caesar the things that are Caeser's, and to God the things that are God's,' he did not make it plain how to interpret it. May God help us!"

They continued in this vein until early evening, with a period of prayer and rest during the afternoon. No soldiers were in sight, so an hour after the sun had set they set off towards Palestrina. The moon shed sufficient light to show their way and the shadows gave sufficient cover to keep them hidden.

As they drew near to the Palestrina fortress they began to be aware of small watch fires regularly spaced around the area, but Benedetto, who was nimble of foot and well practised in the *zelanti* ways of moving through wooded hills and valleys, led them quickly and directly to the secret back stairway which the Colonna party had previously shown them, well hidden from intruders and well fortified from above.

They were challenged as they climbed in single file up to the stout, small door hidden in the wall, but the porter was soon satisfied as to their identity, and showed them into a storeroom where, after receiving some warmed wine, they lay down and slept until after daybreak.

Jacopone now reviewed his situation. He was virtually a prisoner in the fortress, and though he had joined with the protesting group and signed the Longhezza Manifesto, he was already distancing himself from the increasing violent and negative attitude of the Colonna party, and especially from the five French prelates who were in the pay of Philip the Fair of France.

On 16th May, while the three Spirituals had been huddled in their cave above Tivoli, the Palestrina group had issued another and more violent manifesto, directly accusing Boniface of the murder of Celestine in his prison.

Enough was enough for Jacopone, and though the whole group had looked to him as their saintly and charismatic spiritual leader, relationships began to deteriorate in the enclosed conditions of the Palestrina castle. The stress of the situation sharpened tongues, nerves and tempers, and the crude political ambitions of the insurrectionists became plain as their primary motive.

Jacopone continued to be increasingly critical of Boniface, though his reasons for this were becoming clearly less political and more spiritual. As the weeks lengthened into months, through the winter of 1297 and the spring of 1298, he bewailed his lack of discernment and common sense, and longed for the open plain and rolling hills of Umbria.

Being cooped up in this fortress was a heavy penance for his bad judgement. There was only one worse place that he could imagine, and that was the underground series of stinking, damp cells beneath the fortress, which had caused him to shudder one evening when he was exploring the hidden parts of the castle.

Pope Boniface, not satisfied with excommunicating the Colonna rebels, declared open war on them, and in December 1297 preached a crusade against them. From that time he was determined either to starve them out or to breach the walls of the fortress. Time was on his side, so after a few unsuccessful attempts, he waited.

Jacopone realized that there was no hope of escape from such adamantine stubbornness. He knew that Boniface's arrogance far surpassed anything of his own pre-conversion days. There would be no let-up and no forgiveness when the time came.

But Jacopone did not flinch. He set himself the discipline of thinking, praying, writing, and one of the consequences was a diatribe against Boniface, stinging in its rebuke, reflecting more of the reforming friar in Jacopone's nature than that part of himself which he had shared with John of La Verna — the mystical lover of God.

Boniface, already inflamed with anger over the rebellion, was frustrated that efforts to prise out the insurrectionists from their holed-up fortress had failed. His passionate temper had hardened into a cold and settled attitude of calculated determination, and his object was to silence once and for all any question of the validity of his election and claims.

He had not yet issued an excommunication of the three *zelanti* friars, for he had his eye especially on Jacopone da Todi, the popular and sharp-witted preacher. To win him over would be a prize indeed, and he calculated that a few months boarded up with the insecure and weakening insurrectionists would be enough to make him capitulate.

As well as having the Conventual Franciscans on his side, led by Brother Guido of Montefeltro, all but the most stubborn of the *zelanti* Spirituals were now having second thoughts about his succession — for there was no other claimant to the papal throne.

But one morning, as Boniface was occupied with such thoughts as these, the diatribe arrived from Palestrina. It had been pitched over the castle wall, addressed to the pope, and was brought quickly to him in case it contained news of conditions for surrender.

As Boniface read it, his anger mounted, and he felt the pounding of his heart within his chest and the beating of his pulse within his head. It read:

Pope Boniface, you've carried this world in your heart,
You'll not be so merry when the time comes to die.

You'll have earned your dire reward,
Not only in your arrogant life before your accession,
But more especially since you took the papal thone.
In comparison, your former life was modest indeed.

You always coveted riches avariciously,
Robbing rich and poor alike,
Carefully building your house upon sand,
But the day of its downfall approaches.

Just as a salamander renews itself in fire
So you renew yourself in scandal, crime and vice;
What do you care about the souls of men?
But you will care when you see what's prepared for you.

You have ruled with craftiness and guile,
Ridden the world like a horse at your pleasure,
But the day of your downfall will come,
And you will never rise again.

When you said your first mass darkness fell,
Extinguishing lights and candles throughout the land.
On the day of your enthronement forty men were slain,
Revealing God's displeasure.

Like Lucifer, vaunted with pride in heaven
You have challenged the sovereignty of God;
Like him, poisoning the world with blasphemies,
You will be cast down, and all will curse your name.

Neither magic nor scheming can lengthen your life,
For doom comes suddenly to the wicked;
And no pope has behaved so wickedly
And wallowed in sin as you have done.

Cursed be your name and all your wicked works,
You who have cast aside the fear of God;
You who have made so many to suffer
Will suffer at last in pain and despair.

Boniface threw down the parchment to the floor and ground his foot upon it. But he did not forget. "Jacopone envied me as a young man in Todi," he reflected, "and he envies me still. He shall learn that my pent-up anger, when it is unleashed, shall grind him into the ground."

A few months later, in September 1298, a breach was made in the walls of the Palestrina fortress. Ironically the troops were led by Landolpho Colonna, brother to one of the insurrectionist cardinals, helped by Guido of Montefeltro, a Conventual friar.

The insurrectionists, arrayed in mourning, were marched off to Rome to submit to the pope. The cardinals were absolved but deprived of their purple. Palestrina's fortress was razed to the ground and the site sown with salt at the command of the pope, to symbolize barrenness and infertility. But the underground dungeons remained intact!

Jacopone's memory of the wrath of Pope Boniface and the resultant excommunication and imprisonment brought him full circle to his present condition. Here he lay, in one of those very dungeons, and four years had passed.

The horror and fear that had caused him to shiver uncontrollably as he was forced down to his cell had now given way to a gentle passivity. It was not a passivity born of despair or resignation but rather a consequence of trust in the mercy of God.

He no longer felt what he once interpreted as righteous indignation against the pope — rather he felt pity. As for himself, he was content to commit his poor life to God's mercy.

All this was true, and yet as he shifted painfully upon his pallet and the whole panorama of his life unfolded before him, he suddenly felt that the end was not yet! But what else could there be? It was not now likely that Pope Boniface would release him. He had almost reached the point of accepting that the darkness of his cell was leading to his death.

But at that moment of acceptance a new spark of hope was ignited in his heart, and burst into a gentle but powerful flame. He was both perplexed and enthused by such a happening, but he did not have long to wait before a new set of circumstances changed his whole attitude to his confinement and the possibility of release.

Part Two

13   Light in the Cell

One morning footsteps were heard approaching the small grating in the wall of Jacopone's prison — and suddenly they stopped! Looking through the grille, Jacopone came face to face with Pope Boniface. There was no word of hope or healing for Jacopone, only a question, coldly mocking: "Jacopone, when will you come out?" Jacopone replied without malice, but with prophetic discernment: "The day you go in."

Pope and friar looked at one another through the grille — and both men trembled. Jacopone was a bag of bones, gaunt and ascetic in appearance. His cell stank, his body was unwashed and verminous, but he was no longer either arrogant or cringing before the pope. His trembling arose from a profound and new sense of interior strength and courage, and though his words to Boniface were fearless, they were not haughty or vengeful.

Boniface was well fed, perfumed and oiled and dressed in his beautifully tailored ecclesiastical robes. His trembling was brought on by the quiet and firm gaze of his prisoner, and the inward realization that the words he had just heard carried a note of prophetic import.

Suddenly their roles were reversed. Jacopone, after four weary years of imprisonment and deprivation, had entered a new phase of courage and inward freedom. But Boniface, surrounded by political and ecclesiastical intrigue, realizing that the days of papal triumphalism were in rapid decline, trembled with apprehension and fear.

For a moment, exposed nakedly to the truth about one another, Jacopone and Boniface both glimpsed the possibility of redemption, of reconciliation with each other — and even of love.

Jacopone trembled on the edge of opportunity, but before he could utter a word Boniface broke the gaze, turned on his heel and walked quickly away from the cell.

"On such moments hang salvation and damnation," thought Jacopone. He was aware that some power had been put into motion which was to break up all those hard and impenetrable areas left in his soul. This was the new beginning. It was as if the sun had risen upon a freezing world; the ice was beginning to crack and the waters were about to flow again.

Under the influence of this process Jacopone found himself speaking to John of La Verna in his waking and dreaming hours. In mystic communication they traversed again the moutainous terrain of darkness and the absence of God. Jacopone saw that all his years of infidelity and backsliding could be redeemed and caught up into the wider scheme of things. It was all part of the way, of the dark night of purgation. His prison cell had taught him detachment and abandonment to God and the beginnings of naked faith. All these things were landmarks on that spiritual journey from San Damiano to La Verna. Nothing had been wasted. Even his deprivation and suffering had been woven into the pattern of love.

About a month later all this was confirmed. Jacopone's nose suddenly began to twitch. He had become immune to the stench of his cell, but this was a smell which set his heart beating wildly, transporting him in imagination to that day on the holy mountain when John was surrounded by heavenly light and the whole area became fragrant with this same smell.

The iron door swung open and the jailer admitted a man of about forty years of age, spare of frame but radiant with an inward strength. He strode into the cell, fell at the feet of Jacopone, and unashamedly began to weep.

"John my brother!" cried Jacopone, so bewildered and dazzled by the sight and touch of the other that he stumbled, almost falling over him.

John got to his feet, and lifted Jacopone, unconscious of his filthy and unkempt physical condition. They embraced one another, sharing tears of pent-up misery and joy, until the jailer said roughly: "Only half an hour at the most," pocketing the money that John had put into his hand, and locking the door upon them.

After the first rush of emotion had subsided the two men found their tongues, and the twenty years since their first meeting at the convent in Todi yielded up all its hidden treasure of meaning and pain.

"How ever did you manage to get in here?" asked Jacopone.

"I have tried many times," answered John, "only to be turned away with curses, and once beaten and threatened with my life. But over the last month I have heard you call to me and knew that this time I should obtain entrance. And so I have, with no opposition — though I did give a little encouragement to the jailer." He smiled sadly as he looked upon the emaciated state of the prisoner, realizing that many more months of underground incarnation could mean his death.

The most important part of their conversation was the pattern of their spiritual journey, for Jacopone was now well assured that his feet were on the way again, and that their two souls were knit together in reconciliation and love. It was as if they were the two wings of a great eagle which gazed into the glory of the sun.

They both learned from one another, but at one point John said, "Jacopone, in my dire need on the mountain many years ago you held me in God through such desolation as I have not known since. And now, my brother, I have been holding you in love and hope during the long time of your captivity."

He took Jacopone's hand as he continued, and Jacopone lowered his eyes and gazed upon the earthen floor of his cell. "Your darkest captivity began when you became interested, excited and then obsessed with political and ecclesiastical affairs, which beguiled you into using the same tactics and weapons as the enemies of Christ."

"I know it well, my brother," cried Jacopone. "I have spent many sad hours of repentance and remorse in this cell, for strange as it may seem, this captivity has been the means of liberating me from my false and unsanctified self."

"Our Lord liberated you by imprisoning you," responded John, "but I do not underestmiate the bitter cost in pain and darkness. It grieves me, my dear brother, to find you fettered and bound like a captive bird."

"The loss of freedom has caused me untold pain," murmured Jacopone sadly, "especially since it is so long since I have wandered among the Umbrian hills and plains. But the loss of *you* has all but broken my heart. Now you have come to me, my sorrow is turned into joy and I have hope that my beloved Lord will show His face again."

"Not only show His face, Jacopo," responded John, "but draw us to His heart. Your pain and desolation are part of that dark night through which all must pass who seek the embrace of God."

With these words silence fell upon them and they both dropped to their knees. Then, placing their hands upon one another's heads they said the blessing which St Francis had pronounced on Brother Leo so long before:

The Lord bless you and watch over you;
The Lord make His face shine upon you,
    and be gracious to you;
The Lord look kindly on you,
    and give you peace.

No sooner had they got to their feet than the jangle of keys told them that the jailer was signalling the end of the visit. With a swift embrace they took leave of one another and were surprised to hear the jailer say to John, "If you have a mind to come again, father, it would be well to mention the name of Filippo, and say that you have business with me. That will save you some trouble."

Then he lowered his eyes and asked, "Would you give me your blessing, father?" as he fell to his knees. Brother John laid his hands on Filippo's head and blessed him as Jacopone looked on in amazement.

"Heaviness may endure for a night," called John to Jacopone as the cell door clanked shut, "but joy comes in the morning."

During the next few months John of La Verna was allowed to pay two more visits to Jacopone. Filippo's attitude to Jacopone had previously been somewhat rough and cautious, for he too was under surveillance. But with each of John's visits his manner became kinder and he seemed more at peace with himself. His task as jailer of a mad saint was not an enviable one!

One day he brought Jacopone a small cake which he said his wife had baked. This was the first mention of a wife, and as Jacopone took the cake and began to eat it Filippo talked with him.

"You know, brother, that these last four years have not been easy for me," he said anxiously, looking towards his prisoner. "There are some things we are called upon to do that do not always please us. I would be glad to know that you do not hold them against me — for I have had to obey orders — my livelihood depends on it . . ."

Jacopone wiped the crumbs from his mouth and looked at him. "Tell your wife that she bakes a good cake, Filippo," he replied, "and say also that her husband may not surround Jacopone with blessings, but neither does he indulge in curses."

"You speak like your poetry," said Filippo. "I often have to ponder over your words until they give up their meaning."

"Do *you* read my poetry?" questioned Jacopone, wide-eyed.

"Everybody reads the poetry of Jacopone da Todi," smiled Filippo, "and sings his songs." Then he added a significant sentence before he quickly went out and closed the cell door: "I think that you too will begin singing before very long."

When John made this third visit Jacopone told him what Filippo had said, and asked what he could have meant.

"What he means," answered John after a pause, "is that opinion against Boniface is running high in many quarters, and people like Filippo are reading the signs of the times. "Then he added: "But don't be stimulated overmuch by political opinions, Jacopo. There is a power behind nations which ultimately bends them to its will."

"I am duly rebuked, my brother," grinned Jacopone. "In any case, without moving from my cell I have been making a long journey. I don't know whether you brought a renewed sense of the divine love when you came to this cell some six months ago, or whether the divine Love brought you here, but strange things have been happening within me."

"The truth is never only here *or* there," laughed John, "but both here *and* there."

As he said this he looked over to the rough wooden pallet which served Jacopone for a bed and saw the writing materials he had brought him on the previous visit. "Have you begun to write again, Jacopone?" he asked.

Jacopone went over to the pallet and passed a square of parchment to John who took it and spent some time in silence reading the dialogue between Christ and the soul:

Soul

Show Yourself, Jesus Christ!
    You would I find and hold;
    For I have heard it told
        You love me tenderly.

Teach me and lead me on
    To find Your love so sweet;
No longer would I grieve You, Lord,
    By pause, or by retreat:
    Sore have You mourned the tarrying of my feet,
        And waited long for me.

Now open wide the gate,
    That I Your love may seek:
My Life, my Hope, my Jesus Christ:
    Love, turn to me and speak!
    No longer be estranged from one so weak,
        Who prays so longingly.

Christy

    Soul, if you come to Me,
      Hear now then what I say:
    You can be Mine upon the Cross,
      There is no other way.
      There only can you lay your weary head
        With Mine eternally.

Soul

    O Christ, my Love, I climb
      Your Cross, I will not shrink:
    Naked, and wrapt in Your embrace,
      Death's cup with You to drink.
      Joyful in anguish, in Your arms to sink,
        Dying in ecstasy.

John looked up from the page. "I recognize the voice of Jacopone da Todi," he said quietly, "and I am moved because we are both on the way again. But this time — this time, my brother, we are both touched by the same Spirit of flame and caught up in its burning heat."

The colour drained from Jacopone's face. "Oh, do not speak more, my brother," he cried. "I am afraid to speak, to write, to think or to pray. For now, as soon as I give myself to prayer, or talk thus with you, great fear takes hold of me and my very being is threatened."

"You are afraid of love, my brother?" asked John quietly.

"Afraid? — Yes I am," replied Jacopone. "In the same way that you are afraid, John. For it is a frightening thing to fall into the hands of the living God — our God is a consuming fire."

"And what is the proof of the reality of such fear and love?" asked John.

"Look at me!" commanded Jacopone, facing John with a steady gaze.

"Ah, don't gaze so powerfully upon me," pleaded John, "for I see through your eyes and deep into your soul. You are afflicted by the same wound that torments me."

"And another sign that assures me of its rightness," continued Jacopone, "is that I think of Boniface with sorrow, with forgiveness and even with love."

"That is no part of the *old* Jacopone," said John, glad that Jacopone had lifted his gaze, "but a sign of the divine grace and the indwelling Christ."

On his previous visit John had told Jacopone that luxurious beds and soft living were no context for vision and prophetic insight; his words were now confirmed as the cell seemed to light up with a radiance and glory which surrounded the two friars in its embrace.

Jacopone's forgiveness of Boniface came not a moment too soon, for a few days later, on 17th September 1303, five years after Jacopone's incarceration in the Palestrina dungeon, the forces of Philip the Fair of France, supported by the Colonna party, entered Alagna and took Boniface prisoner.

The pope did not last long in French hands. By the beginning of October he was dead, and according to the decree of his hermit predecessor Celestine V, no time was lost in electing a new pope — Benedict XI.

On 23rd October a startling thing happened. Before dawn, Filippo's footsteps were heard running down the steps along to Jacopone's cell. There he stopped, and Jacopone stared at the door in silence. There was a mumbling as if Filippo was talking to himself — or praying!

Then the key rattled in the lock. The door swung open and the jailer lifted his lantern. He stared at Jacopone. His face was marked with anxiety and apprehension. "You are free, master," he said, swallowing his spittle and licking his lips. "The new pope's men have come for you. You are to bathe and dress and be taken to Lord Benedict for absolution and release."

Jacopone understood the jailer's predicament. "Filippo," he said, his eyes moistening, "would you condescend to let me hug you, filthy and vile as I am?"

Filippo gasped, ran towards Jacopone and fell at his feet, clasping his legs. "Oh, Filippo," laughed Jacopone, "I am the emotional man — don't forget that you are a hard taskmaster, and don't hold me so hard. I have been starved in this abominable prison and am not very strong."

Filippo could not take this sudden outburst of humour, and with tears and confession he sought Jacopone's forgiveness. Jacopone lifted him up and held him by the shoulders: "Forgiveness, my friend? There is nothing to forgive. You have done your duty, and though I could have wished for a softer bed, fresher air and more palatable food (saving your good wife's recent baking), you have nevertheless acted for me in the providence of God, and may God grant that we shall be as close in friendship in the future as we have in duty in the past."

Then suddenly, after such light banter, Jacopone's legs gave way, and Filippo sat him down, brought him some wine and then took him and bathed and clothed him in order that he could accompany the pope's emissaries.

October in Umbria. After five weary years in the semi-darkness of a fetid underground prison Jacopone gazed upon the wonder of the world. He was entranced and smitten by its melancholy beauty, for in it, by it and through it the love of God laid siege to his soul.

After his interview with the pope in which he was granted absolution and freedom he had been given sustenance and a bed to rest. The next morning Pope Benedict insisted that he be taken back to Todi by carriage — a journey of about one hundred kilometres.

By the time he reached Todi exhaustion had overtaken him, and Alberto received him at the convent of San Fortunato with tears and joy. He had recently given up his guardianship and therefore had time gently to lead Jacopone back into the rhythm and liturgical life of the friars, and to take him into the surrounding countryside where they would sit hour by hour in silence and adoration of God.

There were times when Jacopone could utter no word, and other times when he would break out into singing and extempore prayer. After being so starved of sensual beauty in his cell, he one day burst forth in spontaneous song:

> *O Love divine, You besiege my heart:*
> *You are crazed with love for me, and cannot rest.*

My five senses are assaulted by You,
Hearing, sight, taste, touch and scent.
Love, You woo me and I cannot hide from You.

I gaze through my eyes and see Love all around
In radiance and colour, in earth, sea and sky,
Drowning in such beauty, You draw me to Yourself.

I open my ears to music,
Entranced by the woven mist of loveliness,
Creation's chanting of Your name.

I taste and savour Your sweetness,
You hunger and thirst for me,
And You are my medicine and food.

Your perfume breathes through all creation,
I am held and wounded by Your odour,
For all creatures give forth the fragrance of Your beauty.

If I stretch out my hands to touch,
You are sculptured in all fair forms,
You inflame me with desire for Your love.

I flee from You and yet I cannot escape,
You yearn to melt me in Your love,
Oh, to be possessed by Love's fiery embrace.

So lead me to Christ, my fair Love,
To share the wounds and griefs that He bore,
Patterned throughout creation.

Jacopone sang these words to the skies from the top of a grassy hill outside Todi as Alberto watched and listened. Afterwards they sat down quietly together.

"You understand now, my brother, something of the way you have come?" asked Alberto. "And that the journey from San Damiano to La Verna is an interior pilgrimage of the soul?"

"I understand a little," replied Jacopone. "But you knew all the time many of the battles I would have to face, didn't you?"

"I knew in my *mind*," replied Alberto, "but only you could traverse such wild terrain, and only by experience could the lesson be learned. To me it is given to know the map, the contours, the terrain of the country, but only to such as you is it given to climb the high places and tread the dark valleys."

"But it is not done yet," added Jacopone quietly. "I feel that I am on the borderland of infinity, trembling with apprehension and yet wounded so deeply that I must cry to the crucified One for healing. I find strange yearnings arising in my heart, clothed with thoughts and words I cannot understand or explain. It is as if there is a whole unexplored world within me, and a language I have never learned giving rise to thoughts and images I cannot explain. My heart affirms what my mind cannot grasp. It is as if I must follow my heart in order for my mind to understand:

Love unutterable,
Good unimaginable,
Light immeasurable
Shine in my heart.

Now where do those words come from, and how can I begin to understand?"

Alberto gazed long and silently at him until Jacopone became uncomfortable. "Why do you look so long and pensively at me, my father," he asked.

"Because I see so many things coming to consummation in you after all these years," Alberto replied. "I have told you that I am a map-reader more than a pilgrim. That does not mean that I have not walked in the foothills and caught glimpses of the heights, but my vocation and duty has been to minister to those ordinary souls who have neither the passion of ecstasy nor the suffering of despair."

"You speak of the *mitigati*?" queried Jacopone with a smile that communicated both humour and understanding.

"Yes the *mitigati*," replied Alberto, "but also the *zelanti* and the *litterati*. What you found difficult to understand, Jacopone, was that allowing for temperamental and social differences, God has His dearest souls in all three parts of our Order, but that for the most part the majority are content to be followers and not blazing pioneers. And my vocation, for good or ill, has been to be their pastor."

"Has this been a sorrow to you, my father?" asked Jacopone, realizing for the first time that Alberto was opening his soul to him.

"Yes, Jacopo," replied the former Guardian. "I have only glimpsed ecstasy and deep darkness. How often I have longed to be touched with the madness that you have known, and to be caught up in the ecstatic glory of the divine Love which moves the sun and stars. I have felt your pain, witnessed your grief, shared sympathetically in your anguished joy at the crucified Jesus. I have been with you in your excesses, turned you from wild and abandoned asceticism and pointed the way to simplicity, moderation and charity. But God has required of me a simple path, reserving the higher way until I am quit of this mortal body."

"You could not have envied the stupidness of my wilderness period," said Jacopone, "when I became obsessed by ecclesiastical affairs, throwing in my lot with the Colonna party. Look where that led me!"

Alberto sighed. "Is it not strange, Jacopone, that those things in which you went most astray were especially used to bring you to the deep darkness which you most needed for detachment, humility and love?"

"Strange indeed," agreed Jacopone. "It certainly accomplished the impossible, but I could wish it might have happened another way."

"I suspect there was no other way — for *you*," said Alberto, gently laying his hand upon Jacopone's arm. "And do you see what is needed now?"

Jacopone looked out over the plain and then lifted his eyes to the sky. It was one of those November days in Umbria when the sun shone clearly through the crisp air, warning of colder days to come.

"Yes, I see a pattern emerging," he said, "though the details are not clear. It seems to me that I must move out of the convent at Todi, with your permission, though my seventy-three years weigh heavily upon me, and it may not be until the spring that I can take my departure. I feel that I should spend some months alone in the hills so that all I have been through should be interpreted to my own soul by the divine Spirit.

"Then perhaps I should meet with John at La Verna again, spending next winter there in order that we should both listen to and learn from one another; for as you saw so long ago, our paths have intertwined remarkably and we are of one mind and soul. And after that? — well, God knows."

"That is the pattern which I also had in mind," commented Alberto. "You need to feed and stretch your mind in the library at San Fortunato, for you are not now afraid of becoming one of the *litterati* party! You have already read widely in Augustine, John Cassian and the fathers of the desert. But there are many others which call for study and I have ever impressed upon you the need to dwell deep within Holy Scripture. I think there is no need for me to warn you of restless activity and the value of silence."

"You remind me of my former obsessions and frustrations," answered Jacopone. "I hope my days of self-seeking activity are over. I do not deny that my preaching and holy madness may have been used in the mercy of God, but I am ashamed of my former emotional evangelism and of my proud penitence."

"Do not be too hard on yourself, Jacopone," said Alberto. "You have had many difficult lessons to learn and a long time of enforced imprisonment in which to learn them."

They remained quiet for a while, then rose and began the leisurely descent down the hill back into Todi, touching on the plans for Jacopone's winter at San Fortunato and his preparation for solitude in one of the hill hermitages in the spring and summer of the following year.

So the time passed while Jacopone immersed himself in Scripture and the fathers, spent time with Sebastiano and some of his old friends and found himself at the centre of a reconciling movement within the *mitigati* convent.

The San Fortunato friars found in Jacopone the same fire that had blazed in the early days of his conversion, but now it was guarded, controlled and burned more clearly without smouldering. He radiated a wisdom, gentleness and joy that all could feel, without the dogmatism and arrogance of former days. He was so sought after that Alberto had to ask the new Guardian to point out that Jacopone's silence must be respected. How things had changed!

One night after Compline, Brother Giorgio found Jacopone silent and still on his knees in the library. His duty was to put out the lights and indicate to any friars there that they should be in their cells.

In front of Jacopone was a manuscript of Dionysius the Areopagite, open at an underscored passage:

Threefold is the way to God. The first is the purgative way, wherein the mind is inclined to learn true wisdom. The second is the illuminative way, wherein the mind by pondering is kindled to the burning of love. The third is the unitive way, wherein the mind by understanding, reason and intellect is led up by God alone.

Jacopone had copied this passage, drawn a cross beneath it and added his own stanzas:

In perfect love three states I see:
Good, better, best they seem to be.
The best, the Ultimate, would be
    Loved undividedly.

The love I ask for is a single fire,
And heaven and earth it fills with its desire.

Giorgio did not undertand what the passage meant, but he felt the power and radiance emanating from the kneeling figure who was perfectly quiet and absorbed in contemplation.

He extinguished the lights and left Jacopone there. As he closed the door he wondered if he had even begun to love God, and as he ascended the stairs he quietly sang one of the poems of Jacopone that he did understand:

> *His time is lost indeed who loves You not,*
> *Jesus, my love, most dear and most divine.*
> The Saviour with none other can compare.
>   Alas, my heart! whose portion is so scant!
> Naught else consoles me — nothing can I care
>   For all the world if only You I want.
> Sweet love of Jesus! all my hope is there!
>   Rule in my heart, lest I should fall, and grant
>   That I may knit Your love more close to mine.

> The heart that loves not You must needs be sad,
>   Jesus, You joy and solace of mankind:
> Christ, without You no spirit can be glad.
>   Ah, wretched me! whose love is chill and blind!
> For if a man all other treasure had
>   Save You, he loses all, and naught shall find,
>   And far from you in bitterness must pine.

> Your splendour gives to all the world its light,
>   And every precious thing reflects Your praise:
> Yes, heaven and earth in You are led aright,
>   Your beauty shines in all ten thousand ways;
> All creatures follow You, and Your own might,
>   — Only the sinner scorns You in his heart:
>   You made him — yet he only is not Yours.

O Saviour, of the gentle Virgin born,
   Great are Your proofs of love, and great Your loss;
Then let me not requite that love with scorn,
   For You did hang for me upon the Cross,
And in Your sacred Hands which nails have torn
   The deed of my salvation did engross,
     Dear Lord, inscribe within my heart that love.

O Fire that makes the soul that You inflame
   To melt away in daily languishing,
There is no tongue can give this wonder name,
   Nor heart conceive, that has not felt its sting.
Alas! my frozen soul denies Your claim:
   Oh, warm my heart, ice-bound and perishing!
     Lest in this cold for ever I should pine.

So Giorgio went to sleep.

14   Union in Love

Springtime in Umbria in the year 1304 was beautiful. For Jacopone there had never been a springtime like this following his five years of imprisonment in the dank underground cell at Palestrina. All his senses were invaded by the natural loveliness and his body was rejuvenated by the rising of the sap, the opening of the buds and the fresh breeze of promise at the heralding of new life in earth and sky. He felt like a newborn soul in the springtime of his life; though he was now in his seventy-fourth year.

It was April before Brother Alberto allowed him to leave for the hills, and even then not before a cell was prepared north of Todi, in the direction of the Poor Clare convent at Collazzone which was to be his base from this time, in order to protect him from his popular reputation among the common people and to preserve the solitude for which he longed.

The cell was a simple wooden structure which had been erected by the few friars who ministered to the Poor Clare sisters, for use as a hermitage through the summer months. It was here that Jacopone spent the months from April to September — months of such solitude and prayer that drew him deeper into God and into himself than had ever before been possible.

While Jacopone was surrounded by people, whether friars or lay folk, he was in demand as a preacher, teacher and counsellor. He responded to such need and gave himself completely, using all his gifts and faculties with boundless energy. He enthused others with an infectious vitality and his times of prayer simply undergirded such ministry and replenished his resources. But when he was alone he experienced within himself a warning and a challenge which he had previously neglected up to the time of his political involvement, but which he had to face during his years of incarceration.

The warning came in the shape of a clear awareness that his life of prayer was lacking in depth and integrity. He sought emotional peak experiences that sustained him for his public ministry, but he lacked order and stability. It was as though he lived by flashes of illumination while neglecting the deeper reaches of communion with God which led to mystical union.

He knew that between such illuminative periods and the higher mystical life lay the dark night in which all fabrications of the false self were stripped away, and in which the soul would be naked before the blazing love of God. But even the thought of such confrontation caused Jacopone to shudder.

But there was also the challenge, the lure. Whenever he was alone for any period of time he found himself descending deep into his own soul, and the old longing for God, the thirst for the infinite, the call of the divine Love seized him once more.

Sooner or later, he knew, he would have to travel that way, to where the inexorable destiny of Love awaited him. One of the most bewildering and ecstatic moments was when he realized that the divine Lover sought him, followed him, wooed him, actually *needed* him. This only intensified his desire and caused him to swoon with yearning.

But all this had been bartered away by his neglect of solitude and the obsession with ecclesiastical politics which had ensnared him and made him a victim of religious worldliness. The life and friendship of John of La Verna were a witness against him during those days, but no word did John speak — he knew that Jacopone had to face this problem alone. The strange thing was that his deliverer had been pope Boniface VIII, and the conditions of the filthy underground prison had proved to be the context of the dark night which set him on the way again.

All that was over now — and with the restoration of springtime the whole pilgrimage of love was again before him.

But before he could share once more with John at La Verna, he needed to learn for himself the lessons that John had learned on the mountain during the intervening years.

The precious friendship had enabled them to give and take within one another's love in as close a manner as was possible this side of heaven. But there were some things that had to be learned alone. John had never looked back, and the darkness and ecstasy that were the pattern of his life had been embraced in the solitudes of La Verna. And now it was Jacopone's turn.

Here was the great gift of solitude — a half year stretching ahead of him before he was to join John on the holy mountain for the winter. These were months in which he would traverse that little-known country between the illuminative and the unitive life which he had glimpsed through the great masters of mystical prayer.

Unlike John, Jacopone found that recording his experiences not only enabled him to understand what had been taking place in his interior life, but also opened up deeper ways into the mystery of God as he wrote. It was as if his mind had descended into his heart and the Spirit of God guided his pen. The whole of the six months in his hermitage enabled him to dwell in solitude in such depth that the result was the writing of what was later recognized as his "torrent of wild loveliness" — the *Amor de Caritate.*

It was during the first two weeks of this solitude that he realized most clearly that he could never reach such heights of glory or such depths of misery while he was continually with people. His incarceration had been the death-blow to his pride, for it was there that he had let go all the pride of reputation and conceit of attachment that had dogged him down the years. There had been no-one and nothing in his prison cell but the facing of death. He had spent many hours meditating over the fate of John the Baptist in prison, incarcerated there by Herod at the whim of a dancing girl. John's powerful ministry had been behind him and the one thing left to be accomplished was martyrdom.

But here in the hills above Todi was the second realization — that solitude was not only necessary for the death of the false self, but also for the quickening of the spiritual faculties of love.

Mystical prayer was a journey, a pilgrimage, but it was an interior journey. He knew that the arduous path from San Damiano to La Verna, though requiring an outward and geographical aspect, involved a far deeper and more painful participation of spirit. It was in those profound and inward places of the soul that confrontation with the living God was effected.

Here also Jacopone learned that just as the divine Love was the power that moved the cosmic circle of the world, so he himself had become a small world, and that what happened in the remaking of his soul in the image of Christ had cosmic effects beyond his wildest imaginings.

Here, on these hills, God in Christ laid hold on Jacopone as long ago the mysterious angel had laid hold on Jacob at Jabbok in mortal combat. Jacopone's written account begins in fire. It is an ecstatic complaint of the infusion and overflowing of divine love, and it is as a lover that Jacopone trembles with the exhilarating passion of a lover's yearning.

The days of asceticism are over and his soul is invaded, distressed and enamoured by love. He is distracted with the madness and foolishness of love — a repetition of the *jubilus* of his early conversion days. But a dynamic, new element enters into the experience.

The poem, *Amor de Caritate* came out of what happened to him with the beginning of his third week of solitude, and it began quite suddenly as the day was ending. Jacopone had climbed up to the top of the hill where his cell was situated, and out of breath he sat down to watch the westering glory of the setting sun.

The disappearance of the sun below the rim of the horizon, and the variegated patterns of the evening sky, always filled Jacopone with strange melancholy and yearning. He could remember in the days of his boyhood, before scholarship, reputation and fastidiousness had obsessed him, feeling that with the setting of the sun he had lost something within his own soul.

On this occasion he lay back on the turf of the hillside and gazed into the sky. Then, without any specific warning, he felt that the pounding of his own heart and the rhythmic spiration of his own breath was in concert and harmony with the life-giving pulse of creative power that he felt in the earth beneath him, in the air around him, in the sky above him, in the setting sun and the rising moon, in the wind and air, the rain and clouds, and in the heave and swell of the sea around the Italian peninsula.

Jacopone knew that the love of the human Jesus reflected the universal nature of the eternal Love which had sought him from his earliest days and tortured him since the moment of Vanna's death. And now he felt himself on the edge of the abyss of that love. In one moment he realized that he could either resist it or abandon himself to it. It was only a moment, and the possibility of decision was overtaken immediately by the bursting of the banks, the overflowing of the torrent, so that he found himself face downward on the hill, and weeping copiously into the grass and soil beneath him. He cried out: "O divine Love, why do you wound me so? My heart is smitten in two, and burns with ardent desire . . ." Many hours later, when he endeavoured to record those first moments of intensity the fire still burned within him:

Glowing and flaming, refuge finding none,
    My heart is fettered fast, it cannot flee;
It is consumed, like wax set in the sun;
    Living, yet dying, swooning passionately,
It prays for strength a little way to run,
    Yet in this furnace must it stay and be:
Where am I led, ah me!
        To depths so high?
        Living I die,
    So fierce the fire of Love.

Before I knew its power I asked in prayer
   For love of Christ, believing it was sweet;
I thought to breathe a calm and tranquil air,
   On peaceful heights, where tempests never beat.
Torment I find, instead of sweetness there!
   My heart is riven by the dreadful heat:
     All words are vain;
     By bliss I'm slain,
   And yet I live and move.

For eighteen stanzas Jacopone wrote in white-hot inspiration, recording what happened as night overtook the evening. They described a cascading torrent of alternating tension and abandonment. They were studded with brilliant and sparkling analogies, expressing the inebriation, confusion, high glory and profound yearning brought about by the infusion of the divine Love within him.

The experience itself ran over into the poem, which was not simply a repeat of the enamoured madness of his conversion, but contained elements of nature and grace which manifested a saturation of the natural by the supernatural. Stanza after stanza called forth the language of fire, torment and ecstasy, full of complaining and yearning, bursting with creative beauty and shuddering with creaturely pain. The longing opened up the soul to an increasing potential and deepening experience, and the poetry built up to an ever-increasing intensity, for there seemed no end to it.

As darkness fell over the hillside and the late April moon and stars shone over the Italian peninsula, Jacopone lay there, sometimes shuddering with tears and longing, sometimes quite motionless in ecstasy, the mountainside below him and the overarching sky above.

The hours passed and the sky became pierced with the first shafts of dawn. Jacopone opened his eyes and sighed with such yearning and desolation that he wondered how much longer he could live in such a state. He was, at the same time, physically tired and yet bounding with vitality and expectation. He got up and ran for a while, danced in the descent to his cell, and then out of breath, for he was an old man now, he sang praises as once more he greeted the sun's rising on a new world.

Throughout the month that followed he could hardly eat or sleep for joy — or for pain. He thought that in this manner he would die, and that, crazed with love for Christ, his spiritual torment would exceed the ability of his old body to keep pace. But it seemed that the incandescent flame of love within illumined and rejuvenated his physical frame — until an abrupt change of mood took place.

It happened like this. In spite of the almost angelic life he had been living, Jacopone endeavoured to eat and sleep and wash. He had stripped to his waist to perform his ablutions one morning at the spring in the mountainside. Touched with a flash of glory he suddenly flung off his clothing completely and immersed himself in the water which was dammed up in a hollow basin below the spring. He cried for sheer joy and wonder, frolicking as a child in the clean, cold waters of the mountainside when, like a thunderbolt from the blue, the word of Christ rang out, shattering the emotional outpouring of his heart with a command to discipline such outrageous spontaneity:

Order this love which burns so violently,
    For without Order virtue comes to naught;
And since you seek Me now so ardently,
    Make virtue to be ruler in your thought,
And by such love summon that energy
    Whose fervours are by gentle Order taught:
    A tree to proof is brought
        By ordered fruit;
        Bole, branch and root,
    All thrive in Order's grove.

Jacopone was smitten speechless as the command continued, showing that only by order and measure in the world can harmony, movement and synthesis reveal the inner meaning of all things. Jacopone listened dripping with water and amazed.

The effect of this dramatic breaking-in of the command of Christ toward order and control was as if a spear had pierced Jacopone's heart. Already exhausted after a month of extreme emotional tension, he felt as though he had scoured the heights and depths of feeling, ransacking the world of analogy and metaphor, and crying through day and night for love of Christ. Therefore he allowed himself to fall upon the ground, and considered this call to order and tranquillity.

There was no doubt that it was the call of Christ, for it sounded from the deepest depths of himself and came with alarming self-validation. He saw also that he had been led, pulled, even dragged through a recapitulation of all his emotional excesses from the time of his conversion — excesses both of ecstasy and despair. And he had arrived at this place of self-evaluation.

During this period time lost all meaning for Jacopone, for he seemed to exist on two levels. He gave himself primarily to listening to what was being spoken within him — the voice of Christ through the voice of his deeper self; and only secondarily did he move mechanically in preparing the basic necessities of food, ablutions and sleep.

He was actually being taught, ministered to directly, by the Holy Spirit, and at this level there was a breathless certitude of communication which did not stir up emotional peaks but transformed the very structures of his being. He felt an actual participation in the divine life, unable to discern where the human ended and the divine began. The borderland of grace and nature became wonderfully blurred.

Measure, rule, rhythm, order. This was the pattern of the cosmos and must be the pattern of his being. He assented to all this. But when he assented fully, then he saw another dimension — that the divine harmony contained playfulness, spontaneity, dance and humour. It was as if the pendulum began to swing again — but this time he saw the excesses of love that were manifest in the Incarnation.

such participation in the divine life. And yet he had taken up his pen while still in the midst of the experience, while words tumbled over one another, cascading in tumultous torrents, and yet with a lucid clarity which belied the discipline and control with which the stanzas and the experience were communicated.

The experience, by its very nature, was indescribable, but language was here stretched to its extreme in some kind of endeavour to communicate, though not accurately to describe, the divine onslaught of Love upon the passive soul.

Jacopone called upon all the beauty of the created order to extol the mystery of the divine Love, and far from this being a rape of the glories of the natural world, every glimpse of loveliness, movement, harmony, light and balance only served to reflect, remind and somehow communicate the glory of the Beloved. And no longer could nature and grace be separated. The natural order served to impart joy and sorrow, elation and yearning, and the world was seen not as illusion, but as manifesting the divine glory, and yet as finite and fading in the light of eternity.

As Alberto and Sebastiano prepared the rough altar, Jacopone began very quietly to sing one of his earliest and simplest songs to a child-like tune which Sebastiano remembered from his boyhood games at school in Todi:

Jesus, my Love, You Flower of Purity,
Born in the field of fair Virginity,
You are the Lily of Humanity,
Full radiantly,
    All fragrant and adored.

Adored the fragrance that from Heaven You bore,
Heaven, the fair garden where You bloomed of yore;
Yea, God the Father sent You through this Door,
Wreathed o'er and o'er
    And twined with many a flower.

203

A Flower of Nazareth was first Your Name,
And from the Rod of Jesse blooming came,
Springing in time of flower; and all Your aim
Love, like a flame,
  On humankind to shower.

To shower His glorious Love most infinite;
In Christ His Son, my Lord, You are my Light;
Mankind to God You draw, and then unite,
And all delight
  You give, and fill with love.

Jacopone responded throughout the liturgy of the mass. He listened to the Gospel, received the Body and Blood of Christ, and rested within the peace of God.

Alberto was aware that he had come through such an onslaught of spiritual experience that had made him very weak. Indeed he wondered at first if the old man's body could survive the demands made upon it. But following the mass, he shared the meal which the others had prepared and answered intelligently all the questions asked of him, though he volunteered no conversation.

The two friars left supplies for Jacopone and he nodded as they urged him to feed himself regularly until they should see him on the next sabbath day. So they took their leave.

On the way down the hill they were silent for a while, and then Sebastiano spoke: "Father, I feel as the three disciples must have felt when they descended the mount of transfiguration. What have we seen today? In what glory have we basked? And what power did Jacopone radiate as we broke bread with him? He sang a little and hardly spoke, but what power he communicated to my poor soul! I am afraid, yet deeply moved and filled with strange awe and joy."

Alberto smiled, and put his hand upon the younger friar's shoulder from the donkey on which he rode, and thus they returned to the *mitigati* convent in Todi. But in his ears and in his heart Alberto heard the words of one of the last six stanzas of

Jacopone's torrent of wild loveliness:

> Love, Love, O Love, the world's wild voices cry,
> Love, Love, O Love, the clamorous echoes spread;
> Love, Love, O Love, so deep Your treasures lie,
> We hunger more, the more we taste Your bread:
> Love, Love, O Love, You Circling Mystery,
> Who enters You at Love's deep heart is fed;
> You're Loom, and Cloth, and Thread:
> O sweet to be
> Clothed radiantly,
> And ceaseless chant of Love.

Mount La Verna, in the region of Tuscany, at the end of September 1304, was ablaze with the soft glory and mellow colours of autumn. The faithful little donkey, Enrico, which Jacopone had brought with him, he left with a peasant family near the base of the mountain, while he, pack on his back, picked his way over the deceptively soft ground on the lower part of the mountain.

His first visit had disclosed the top of the mountain covered with flurries of snow as the winter set in. That had been when Brother John was a prophecy in the mouth of Leo and a dream in the mind of Mario. On his second visit he had been greeted by torrents of rain, and John was undergoing the purgation of the dark night. Jacopone remembered sharing his own pain with him and being the witness of John's restoration to joy and peace. This third visit was in the blazing beauty of autumn, and whatever else awaited him, it was to share with John the mystical indwelling of the Christ who had become the centre of their vision.

As Jacopone stumbled along he recalled how this mountain had been given to Francis, who owned nothing else! In 1213 Francis and Leo had been evangelizing in the vicinity of Montefeltro when they saw crowds of people on their way to the great castle to share the festivities celebrating the knighthood of one of the young men there. They had both joined the throng and found themselves within the large quadrangle, surrounded by banners and music in preparation for the great feast.

One of the troubadour knights had just sung a song of love and suffering for the sake of his love, including the words:

Tanto e il bene ch'aspetto
Ch'ogni pena m'e diletto . . .

During the applause, Francis jumped on to the low wall and taking up the very same words, he began:

So great is the happiness I look for,
that every pain is a pleasure . . .

and he preached on the sufferings of the apostles, martyrs, confessors and knights of Christ, who endured much pain for the glories of the love of Christ. He so enthused the knights, nobles and ladies who heard him, that their thoughts were turned to the eternal kingdom. As a result, the young Count of Chiusi, Orlando, dedicated his life to God, and joyfully made over to Francis his mountain in Tuscany which, as the friars said later, was *molto divota, e molto atta a contemplare*, a very devout and apt place for contemplation.

Jacopone smiled to himself as he thought of the links in the chain of contemplative friars who had lived in prayer and holiness on mount La Verna since the year of the holy stigmata in 1224. He struggled onwards, having to rest often, for although he had great powers of endurance for his seventy-four years, the last months had subjected his mortal body to the consuming fire of the divine Love. Flesh and blood pays a costly price for such ecstasy, and there were times when it had seemed to Alberto that Jacopone's flesh became transparent with bodily rapture, while his senses were in abeyance.

It was this wisdom which called and drew Jacopone to La Verna again, and especially for the Feast of the Exaltation of the Holy Cross on 17th September, to share with John for the last time (well he knew it!) the solitude of communion at the sacred site of the stigmata.

John! Even as Jacopone spoke his name under his breath there was a movement in the trees a few metres on the path above, as Brother Bruno pulled aside some branches to allow Brother John to run forward and take Jacopone in his arms. He did not need to be told that the great borderland had been crossed, and that Jacopone had entered into that third heaven of union with God.

They spoke one another's names and for a full minute remained quite still in embrace without a further word. Then Bruno emerged from the trees with one of the sturdy donkeys that were kept on the mountain, and set Jacopone on its back for the last part of the journey.

Bruno felt the power and the outshining radiance of both these friars as they ascended the mountain with few words of conversation. He and the other friars were now used to the quiet but powerful presence of Brother John — so different from the passionately emotional young friar who had been sustained through heights and depths of ecstasy and dark perplexity over the twenty or so years since his first arrival at La Verna.

Here was Jacopone back again — and what trials and absurdities had overtaken him since his last visit! The La Verna friars were not judgemental about his political entanglement, but they knew well that that long episode corresponded to the forty years' wandering in the wilderness when the Israelites had left the land of Egypt and were continually frustrated by their unbelief from entering into the promised land.

They also knew that this had been the means of great grief and pain to John, who had continually held up his brother in prayer and love, until he had gained entrance into the prison cell where light had entered and the healing process had begun.

Over these years Mario the Guardian had been the mainstay of the community of friars on La Verna and of Brother John, though he knew that the radiance that shone from John's adoration and intercession was God's gift of grace to the whole community.

207

Mario was now an old man, but he received Jacopone with quiet joy and beaming countenance. "After all we have been through, my dear brother, you have come to us again," he said. "The long journey is almost complete. You have fought the good fight, finished the course and kept the faith . . ."

"You speak as if Brother Jacopone is ready for heaven," interjected Bruno with a mischievous smile. "He has many years of service before him yet."

"No, my brother," replied Jacopone, smiling himself at Bruno, "I think we all know that I shall not visit La Verna again, and I am ashamed to be compared to the veteran warrior St Paul — I think his battle scars were more honorable than mine."

Mario ushered them into what had become the main refectory for the La Verna friars, though much of their time was still spent in solitude. They ate together — Mario, John and Jacopone, and agreed that after mass the next day they would meet to plan Jacopone's time on the mountain.

When, the next morning, Brother John celebrated mass, Jacopone watched his face as he repeated the sacred words and elevated the host and chalice. It seemed as if Leo was there again, in one of those long silences which carried him at last into the presence of his beloved Lord.

It was of Leo and Rufino that they both spoke afterwards, during the whole day of sharing. Both Jacopone and John knew that there was not much room for words any longer. They had both entered into the land of solitude in which even the physical proximity of the other was no longer necessary.

But this day was one of retrospect, of tracing the path of their pilgrimage from the vantage-point of La Verna and of affirming the reality and near-completion of the vision vouchsafed to them by Leo.

Jacopone was reluctant to speak, but John led him gently into the verbal sharing of what they already knew, so that they could participate together in the next few months on the mountain, and part when the time came, in a spirit of loving detachment in which they would possess all things in Christ.

"The journey has been long and difficult for you, my brother," said John, "as Leo prophesied it would be. And we both know that this is the last great milestone for you."

"The journey from San Damiano to La Verna," murmured Jacopone. "Yes, I feel it coming to its end, and beyond this the great silence of eternity and the embrace of God."

"Already words fail us," responded John, "for the vision of God already shines within your soul and embraces me with its glory."

"But you, John," said Jacopone, "your end is not yet. This is the last great milestone of our sharing upon earth, but you will carry the primitive vision of our father Francis beyond the confines of our Order and out into the world. You will not sully or mar it by obsessions of power or in righteous indignation that cloaks the hypocrisy of self-love."

John did not contest Jacopone's evaluation of his own failure, but assured him of the grace which redeems those who are elected to the vision of God. "How could I have continued," he asked, "if it had not been for your tender love and sensitive undertanding of my pain and darkness? We have found in one another the human support and mutual strength without which neither of us could have endured. For without human love the divine Love has no meaning for us poor mortals."

As their conversation continued, they began to feel the powerful presence of the Other who promised that where two were gathered in His name, He would be there in their midst — even within them.

Thus the conversation led gently to the rhythmic pattern of solitude, separately and in the sharing of silence and contemplation on different parts of the mountain throughout the months of winter and into the spring of the year 1305.

The milestone of which John had spoken was clearly marked at the beginning of this time — the Feast of the Exaltation of the Holy Cross on 17th September. Both John and Jacopone gathered with the friars before dawn for the community mass celebrated by Brother Mario.

After the reading of the Gospel, most of the lights in the chapel were extinguished and the brothers waited for the Guardian to preach a homily. As they waited Jacopone heard a voice which he recognized as that of Ubertino of Casale who had been in trouble with the authorities for expressing "his fierce indignation at the indifference, luxury and worldliness which were corroding the life of the Order and of the Church . . ." Jacopone smiled gently as he remembered their indignant and political conversations of the past, but all this was forgotten as Ubertino's fine voice filled the chapel, reading the prayer which Francis had prayed in the early morning of the year 1224 on that very mountain:

> O my Lord Jesus Christ, two graces do I pray Thee to grant unto me before I die: the first, that while I live I may feel in my body and in my soul, so far as is possible, the sorrow, sweet Lord, that Thou didst suffer in the hour of Thy most bitter passion; and second, that I may feel in my heart, so far as may be possible, that exceeding love wherewith, O Son of God, Thou wast enkindled to endure willingly for us sinners, agony so great.

Neither Jacopone nor John heard what Brother Mario preached in his homily, and apart from receiving the communion of the Body and Blood of Christ, they hardly knew where they were.

The rest of the day was spent at the place where the stigmatization had taken place, and when one by one the other friars left as evening gave way to night, both John and Jacopone were held there — not now in any excess of emotion, but in that still centre which had become the creative source of their life in Christ.

They spent that vigil of darkness at the most sacred place on the holy mount, and in spirit they were transported to another mountain — that of Calvary where Christ had offered up His life-blood in sublime and perfect sacrifice for the sins of the whole world.

It was not enough for John and Jacopone that Christ had done this on their behalf. They were drawn by such love, in such a way, that with Francis they sought to enter themselves into mystical union with the Saviour on the cross of Calvary. The mysterious words of St Paul inspired them in such a quest: ". . . that I may know Him, and the power of His resurrection, and the fellowship of His sufferings, being made conformable unto his death."

The dawn of the next morning broke over the mountain, the light streaking the sky over La Verna. The beauty and splendour of that Tuscan dawn reflected the new life into which both the friars had entered. One of the poems that Jacopone had written during his previous few months near Collazzone to communicate to John the wonder of participation in the divine Life contained the stanza clearly illustrated by their contemplative stillness at La Verna's shrine:

When the mind's very being is gone,
    Sunk in a conscious sleep,
    In a rapture divine and deep,
  Itself in the Godhead lost —
It is conquered, ravished and won!
    Set in Eternity's sweep,
    Gazing back on the steep,
Knowing not how it was crossed —
  To a new world now is it tossed,
      Drawn from its former state,
     To another, measureless, great —
       Where Love is drowned in the Sea.

Such mystical and transcendent glory did not leave them passively inert, for as the sun rose over the horizon they greeted its rising with gladness, and with the other friars of La Verna, entered into the alternating rhythm of manual work, study and liturgical prayer.

15   Going Home

Jacopone spent the months from September to May on the mountain. He and John shared some of the liturgical life of the other friars and had their own areas of manual work. But Mario gave them permission to make solitude and prayer the primary pattern of their days and nights.

After their initial meeting and the mutual affirmation which led up to the Feast of the Holy Cross there was no further need for words. The more they lived in wordless communication of mind and spirit the more they were able to penetrate one another's souls, sharing the mind of Christ. It was not that their individuality was lost, but that the sense of solidarity with one another was embraced. At the same time they felt drawn into a deeper awareness of the world's beauty and pain, and at the level of adoration and intercession they became instruments of prayer and reconciliation. It was as if, acting as "christed souls" they were participating in the redemption of the world through Christ.

Both were aware that for John there lay ahead a wider ministry of prayer and teaching in the world, while for Jacopone the deepening of his contemplative life was the preparation for the embrace of God in putting off his mortal body.

Mario exercised his ministry as Guardian, observing and guiding from a distance, fully aware of the treasure in earthen vessels which had been entrusted to his care. He realized that the spirits of Francis and of Leo had become incarnate in these two friars, and the vision was as clear as ever on the mountain.

As the year turned and moved into the spring and early summer of 1305, the three of them felt that Jacopone's time on La Verna was coming to an end. On the day of his departure it was agreed that he would leave the mountain quietly, taking leave of Brother Mario in private, while Bruno and John accompanied him to the foot of the mountain where he was to collect Enrico the donkey from the peasant family with whom he had left it.

When they came within sight of the peasant hut, Bruno turned back, leaving John and Jacopone under a birch tree to bid one another farewell. They hardly knew what to say, but Jacopone took from under his habit one of the poems he had penned during the months on La Verna, and gave it to John. It was appropriately called *Love That Is Silent:*

Love, silent as the night
Who not one word will say
To those who have not sight!

O Love, you lie concealed
Through heat and storm and cold
So none may guess or read
Your secrets manifold;
Lest thieves should soon grow bold
To steal away your treasure,
Snatch it and take to flight!

Hidden, your secret fires
More ardently shall glow;
And he who holds you close
Your fiercest heat shall know.
But he who shouts abroad
Your mysteries, will be wounded,
Scorched by your fiery might.

The man who strives to tell
His secret joy within,
In babbling he breaks forth;
Before his words begin
The bitter winds of sin
Will storm and whirl around him,
And wreck his treasure bright.

Let Silence, at your door
　　Hold captive all your sighs;
For Love has set him there,
　　And will not let him rise;
　　So shall you hold your prize
　　　　That it may live within you,
　　　　　　Not scattered left and right.

For if your sighs come forth
　　Then follows on your mind
To wander far from home
　　Leaving true Love behind;
　　So shall you never find
　　　　That inward, perfect Love,
　　　　　　That Treasure Infinite.

John received the poem, smiled into Jacopone's eyes and said: "This will tell me all that needs to be said, my brother. We both know this is not our last farewell — there will be one more. This only would I say — when you have need of me, call my name and I will come to you."

They embraced for a moment in silence. Then John began the ascent of the mountain, while Jacopone walked slowly to the hut to collect Enrico. The donkey stood in the yard, its ears flicking off the flies, and standing by its side was Bruno. "You don't so easily get rid of me," he grinned. "I'm delivering you safe to Colazzone — under obedience to Mario."

Jacopone smiled at the kind deception, and sat down at table with Bruno and the man of the house, while his wife set some refreshment before them, chattering happily. And within the hour, they started on their journey home.

Going home. Umbria, the green heart of Italy, was Jacopone's place of rest. In the small convent at Collazzone, perched in the hills above Todi, he could view the hills which had surrounded him from his earliest days, and the town where he had grown up in the time of his innocence.

Such stories had circulated in Todi and the surrounding villages that people stood in awe of Jacopone. They remembered his former prophetic power, his days of madness, his denunciations of clerics and politicians and his colourful rhetorical preaching — to which many owed their conversion. And now the stories of his holiness and mystical fervour created in the common folk an anticipation of a new and fiery John the Baptist.

There were now no cries of "*Pazzo, pazzo,*!" as there had been in the old days, but quiet, expectant groups of people gathered as the news of his approach ran before him. The people were not disappointed, though they were greatly surprised, for Jacopone manifested a simple and human gentleness. His words were few, and those mostly to the children. But the people wondered at the frailty of his body and luminosity of his eyes.

In the convent at Collazzone he was lovingly received by the sisters, and given a small cell and patch of garden behind the main building. There were three other friars who did some of the manual work of the convent and acted as confessors and chaplains to the sisters — brothers Guido, Leonardo and Luigi. They added the care of Jacopone to their daily duties, and after a few days' rest Bruno returned to La Verna, paying a visit to Brother Alberto at Todi on the way.

From that time Jacopone's life was more inward and uneventful. Outwardly he was simple, courteous and silent, unless spoken to. He managed his patch of garden, gave some time to the few who came to him for counselling, but mostly spent his time in prayer and solitude.

He ate little and spent many nights in vigil, but did not practise any extreme asceticism, preferring to preserve his strength for his daily tasks.

One day Brother Alberto came unannounced to the Collazzone convent from San Fortunato, and found Jacopone working in the vegetable patch behind his cell. As he came near he saw that he was weeping.

"Why do you weep, my brother?" he asked with concern. "I weep because Love is not loved," replied Jacopone. That answer stayed with Alberto for the years that remained to him, and he told it to those who had not been privileged enough to meet Jacopone during this period of his mystical life.

Gradually, as the year of 1306 progressed Jacopone became more frail in body and more childlike in spirit. All the arrogance and conceit of his pre-conversion days, the dogmatism and madness of his first years as a Christian, the wild ascetical excesses and emotional swings of his evangelistic days and the judgemental indignation of his political involvement — all these had given way to the illumination of grace and the mystical life of union with God.

He had no more to say, though sometimes he would weep and sing. At last even his pen was laid aside. It would have been difficult for anyone who did not know Jacopone to believe that he could write the profound poem of fire and ecstasy entitled *Sopr'onne Lengua Amore, Ineffable Love Divine,* which clearly proved that he had pierced that veil into the divine Love which mortal imagination can hardly begin to comprehend. But though he ceased to speak or write in such transcendent language, the reality which lay within, behind and beyond the words suffused his being:

As air becomes luminous,
When filled with the light of day;
As wax dissolves away,
In the heat and glow of fire:
So the soul grows glorious,
Fused in that Heavenly Ray;
No action can it essay,
Gone are its Will and Desire.
The Height that is ever higher
Absorbs its heart and its breath,
It is living, yet lives in death,
Is vanquished in victory.

For wine poured into the sea,
  A man may search in vain;
  There is left of it not a stain
  In the ocean waves that roll.
Itself no more can it be,
  Nor does it ask to regain
  Its former essence again;
  It must give its being in toll.
So Love has drunk the Soul,
    And Truth has changed it so,
    All that it was must go,
      It gives its self in fee.

The first weeks of December were cold and damp in the hill country of Collazzone, and one evening Brother Guido looked in to see if Jacopone needed anything. He found him lying on the threshold between his cell and garden. His breathing was laboured and his face flushed, with beads of perspiration covering his face and forehead.

Guido quickly called for Leonardo and they laid Jacopone on his pallet in the cell while Luigi went to fetch the convent's physician from Collazzone. The physician diagnosed an inflammation of the lungs with attendant fever, and recommended that Jacopone be taken to the convent sick quarters where he could be nursed more easily but with sufficient privacy.

The three friars elected to look after him, working out a rota system with some help from the sisters when necessary. But Jacopone's condition deteriorated quickly and it soon became clear that his life was in danger.

The morning of Christmas Eve arrived, and after Guido and Leonardo had bathed Jacopone's body with cool cloths, his breathing became a little easier and he sunk into a deep sleep.

As the day wore on the friars found themselves talking in undertones, for they felt a strong sense of holiness and awe pervading the room. Jacopone woke and slept fitfully and intermittently, but they sensed an aura of tranquillity which surrounded him, so that he would open his eyes and smile at them, sometimes replying to a question, and then surprisingly he would falteringly sing or pray audibly.

Stillness and waiting held them all as the time drew near to celebrate the Saviour's Incarnation at the midnight mass, but the three friars decided to stay together and receive communion from the community mass after the priest had communicated the congregation, for Jacopone's sick room was quite near the convent chapel.

16   Christmas Eve at Collazzone

Jacopone was dying. The three friars who attended him were aware that he was almost at the point of surrendering his spirit. But there was one more thing to be done. Jacopone had not made his confession and received the *viaticum*, the last Holy Communion which would usher him into the nearer presence of his God.

He had refused Guido's offer in the moments of consciousness, saying: "No, no, not yet . . . it is not time . . . I will wait . . . for my friend . . . he will come . . . blessed John of La Verna . . . from his hand I would receive this grace."

The friars accepted his word though they knew that no-one had informed Brother John of Jacopone's dying condition, for he was over a hundred kilometres away in Tuscany.

They believed that, although Jacopone's physical illness had brought him to his present state, yet he was really dying of an excess of love for God. During the day of Christmas Eve he murmured and sang of love, and would then lapse into periods of unconsciousness. The physician told the friars that in such a way his strength would ebb, and he would quietly take leave of his mortal body.

Brother Leonardo felt in his bones that this was not going to be the end of the story, and that some clear sign of God's grace would intervene to help Jacopone and assure them that all was well. He was certain that the Lord would not leave him alone in his dying hour but enable him to die well.

The snow began to fall outside, and Luigi went to pull the covering more closely around the window. But as he did so, he suddenly cried out with great excitement, "Guido, Leonardo, I see two figures coming up to the convent gate and they are wearing the habits of friars minor . . ."

A pause, and then: "One of them is Brother John of La Verna! Jacopone knew all the time, blessed be God . . ."

Brothers Bruno and John from La Verna gained admission and were soon at Jacopone's side, with oil, prayers and sacrament.

"My brother Jacopo," whispered John gently but clearly, taking his hand in his own, "you called me, and I have come."

Jacopone opened his eyes and smiled. "Oh John, you have come," he responded. "I have been waiting for you — and I am ready . . ."

Quietly, slowly, gently, John led Jacopone into making his last confession. He spoke the saving words, "*Absolvo te,*" in the name of the Holy Trinity, anointing him with oil, communicating him with the Body and Blood of Christ, and kissing him upon the forehead.

At that moment from the convent chapel the voice of the priest was heard intoning the *Gloria* of the mass of Christ's nativity: "*Gloria in excelsis Deo . . .*"

Jacopone responded: "Father, into Your hands I commend my spirit," and breathed his last.

John of La Verna fell on his knees before the body of Jacopone his beloved friend, tears of joy mingling with tears of grief as he sang lines from Jacopone's *Song of Christ's Nativity*:

Music fills the midnight sky,
    "Glory be to God on high!"
    Sing the voices resonant.
    "And on earth there shall be peace,
    Strife shall die and wars shall cease,
    All the world be jubilant!"
Then together let us sing,
Laud and honour to our King,
    Christ, adored and blest is He.

One hundred and twenty-seven years later, in the year 1433,

Jacopone's remains were translated to the Church of San Fortunato in Todi. His tomb, which still exists, carries the inscription:

Ossa Beati Jacopone de Benedictis Tudertini, Fratris Ordinis Minorum, qui stultus propter Christum, nova mundum arte delusit et coelum rapuit.

The bones of the blessed Jacopone dei Benedetti of Todi, of the Order of Friars Minor; who, a fool for Christ's sake, by a new artifice cheated the world, and took heaven by storm.

How the Soul Complains to God of the Over-ardent Love Infused in Her

O divine Love,
Why do You wound me so?
My heart is smitten in two,
And burns with ardent desire.

Glowing and flaming, refuge finding none,
  My heart is fettered fast, it cannot flee;
It is consumed, like wax set in the sun;
  Living, yet dying, swooning passionately,
It prays for strength a little way to run,
  Yet in this furnace must it stay and be:
  Where am I led, ah me!
    To depths so high?
    Living I die,
  So fierce the fire of Love.

Before I knew its power I asked in prayer
   For love of Christ, believing it was sweet;
I thought to breathe a calm and tranquil air,
   On peaceful heights, where tempests never beat.
Torment I find, instead of sweetness there!
   My heart is riven by the dreadful heat:
      All words are vain;
     By bliss I am slain,
   And yet I live and move.

For I have lost my heart, my will, my wit,
   My hopes, desires, my pleasures and my taste;
Beauty seems vile, corruption crawls on it,
   Riches, delights and honours all are waste:
A Tree of Love, with fruits both fair and fit
   To feed me, in my heart is rooted fast,
   It flings away in haste
      All it can find,
     Will, strength, and mind:
   With Love in vain I strove.

All that I had, to purchase Love I gave,
   Yes, all myself, and the whole world in fee;
And had Creation been all mine to have,
   For Love would I have given it willingly:
Now Love has tricked and caught me, woeful slave;
   Emptied of all, I know not where I be;
   Yes, Love has ruined me,
      All crazed my thought;
     I am sold for naught,
   Beggared and script by Love.

My friends, who loved me, called me oft away,
    Far from this bitter path, this arid track;
But how can kingship sink to serfdom? nay —
    Who gives himself has given, and takes not back.
Marble may sooner melt and turn to clay,
    Than Love, my Jailer, loose me from His rack;
    My Will, a broken wrack,
        Love has ignited,
        Transformed, united;
    Who can endure You, Love?

Now are we one, we are not separate;
    Fire cannot part us, nor a sword divide;
Not pain nor death can reach these heights so great
    Where Love has snatched and set me by His side:
Far, far below, I see the worlds gyrate,
    Far, far above, my heart is satisfied:
    My soul, who is your Guide
        To this strange bliss?
        'Tis Jesu's kiss,
    All sweetness far above.

Now on no creature can I turn my sight,
    But on my Maker all my mind is set;
Earth, sea, and sky are emptied of delight,
    For Christ's dear love all else I clean forget:
All else seems vile, day seems as dark as night;
    Cherubim, seraphim, in whom are met
    Wisdom and Love, must yet
        Give place, give place,
        To that One Face
    To my dear Lord of Love.

Therefore let none reprove me evermore,
    If Love so wondrous craze me utterly;
How can my heart withstand these onslaughts sore?
    Besieged and taken thus, how can I flee?
My heart must break; think, friends, what pains it bore!
    Can I endure this furnace patiently?
    You who give ear to me,
        And pity take,
        Your hearts would ache,
    If I my woes could prove.

For heaven and earth and all things else do cry
    That Love is all my task, my life, my place;
Their heartfelt voices cry aloud — "Draw nigh!
    The Love that made you, hasten to embrace!
That Love that thirsts for you eternally,
    Commands us, to His arms your soul to chase;
    He pours His light and grace,
        And ecstasy
        Full radiantly,
    In spreading streams of Love!"

More would I love, if more were possible;
    Yet can I give no more than all my heart;
I give my all — my life, my soul, my will,
    Nor needs it proof that all is more than part.
I give You all, O Lover Terrible —
    Take all, fresh life for ever to impart;
    So old, so new, You are;
        Yes, I have found You,
        Soft light around You,
    And whiter than the Dove.

Gazing on You, You Bright and Morning Star,
    I am led far, and naught else can I see;
My heart is melted, like a waxen bar,
    That moulded in Christ's likeness it may be;
O Christ, Your bargains keen and wondrous are!
    I am stript naked, thus clothed in You to be:
    My heart transformed in me,
        My mind lies dumb,
        To see You come
    In sweetness and in Love.

So coupled with that sweetness is my mind,
    It leans and strains, its Lover to embrace:
And all in Him, and naught in self to find,
    It learns, by gazing ever on His face.
Riches, and powers, and memories strong to bind,
    It casts away, as burdens in the race;
    It has no resting-place,
        No will, no care;
        It mounts the stair,
    Towards which its being strove.

In Christ transformed, almost my soul is Christ;
    Conjoined with God, all, all is now divine,
And I, dear Lord, no longer can resist,
    Beholding now Almighty Love's design:
Nor need I now, set free from mortal mist,
    Ask medicine for the guilt that once was mine;
    No more in grief I pine,
        My sinful soul
        Is purged and whole,
    Yes, it is cleansed and shrove.

Now, a new creature, I in Christ am born,
    The old man stripped away — I am new-made;
And mounting in me, like the sun at morn,
    Love breaks my heart, even as a broken blade:
Christ, First and Only Fair, from me has shorn
    My will, my wits, and all that in me stayed,
    I in His arms am laid,
        I cry and call —
        "O Christ, my All,
      O let me die of Love!"

For you, O Love, my heart consumes away,
    I cry, I call, I yearn for Your caress;
Living, I perish when You do not stay,
    Sighing and mourning for my Blessedness:
When You return, I strain and strive and pray,
    To lose amidst Your All my Nothingness:
    Then tarry not to bless,
        Bind with Your love
        My will, sweet Lord,
      Consume my heart with Love!

O Love most gentle, look upon my pain,
    How can I suffer all Your dreadful heat?
All crazed I am, close fettered by Love's chain,
    I know not what I say, nor Whom I greet:
Fevered, amazed, to wander I am fain,
    In anguish oft, and dragging weary feet;
    I have no strength to meet
        This torment's tide;
        My heart is dried,
      And like an empty glove.

My wits are stolen away: I cannot grasp
 What things I ought to do, or may have done;
The world is strange to me, I strive to clasp
 Love bodiless, if Christ but lead me on:
If not, my joy were but a venomous asp;
 My mind, entangled, loses all it won,
 Yes, Love has left me none
   Of all my skill,
   My speed, my will;
  He takes them all for love.

I once could speak, but now my lips are dumb;
 My eyes are blind, although I once could see:
In this abyss my soul is stark and numb,
 Silent, I speak; cling, yet You capture me:
Falling, I rise; I go, and yet I come:
 Pursue, and am pursued; I am bound yet free;
 O Love overwhelming me!
   Maddened I cry:
   "Why must I die,
  Your fiery strength to prove?"

(*Christ speaks*)
Order this love which burns so violently,
 For without Order virtue comes to naught;
And since you seek Me now so ardently
 Make virtue to be ruler in your thought;
And by such love summon that energy
 Whose fervours are by gentle Order taught:
 A tree to proof is brought
   By ordered fruit;
   Bole, branch and root,
  All thrive in Order's grove.

For see, with number and with balance fit,
   I order, in the world, things near and far:
From end to end fair Order measures it,
   That all may move in peace, and not in war;
Then should not Love in ordered sweetness sit?
    Love, of her nature steadfast as a star?
    Your frenzy sore does mar
       Your fervours, Soul,
       You are not whole,
    Have not controlled your love.

(*The Soul answers*)
Christ, Who has stolen my heart, You call on me
   In order fair my trembling mind to set;
You draw me on, I cry so piteously —
   Never was such a bargain driven yet!
As skies at sunrise, shining lucently,
   Or iron that the piercing flame has met,
   Their native form forget,
       In wondrous change,
       So I, O strange!
    Am dipped and clothed in Love.

So, when a soul its self-hood has quite lost,
   Of its own will no action can it take;
Of all its deeds that Power must pay the cost
   Who has remade it, and does still remake;
Then, if my soul upon Your bridge has crossed,
   O Christ, from Self's false dream in You to wake,
   I do all for Your sake,
       And if You rue
       What now I do,
    'Tis Your own doing, Love.

And this I tell You, Love, if I be crazed,
   You, Wisdom's self it is, that crazes me;
'Twas You that pierced me, You on whom I gazed,
   The bargain that we made is all my plea:
On that new life I entered, all amazed,
   Stript of myself, clothed in divinity;
   Undone, from self I flee;
      Strong for Your sake,
      The doors I break,
    And reach Your breast, O Love!

Why did You lead me to this bed of fire,
   If You would have me calm and temperate?
You gave Yourself, Yourself, to my desire,
   And so my raptures never can abate:
To clasp You little, Love, I did aspire,
   How can I bear it when I clasp You great?
   If this a fault You rate,
      Yours is the blame,
      For in Your name
    I tread this path, my Love.

Yourself from Love Your Heart did not defend,
   From Heaven to earth it brought You from Your throne;
Beloved, to what sheer depths did You descend,
   To dwell with man, unhonoured and unknown:
In life and death to enrich us without end,
   Homeless and poor, with nothing of Your own,
   You trod Your path alone,
      For You were called
      By Love unwalled,
    That all Your heart did move.

For as about the world Your feet did go,
    'Twas Love that led You, always, everywhere;
Your only joy, for us Your love to show,
    And for Yourself no whit at all to care;
You stood within the Temple, calling, "Ho!
    All you who thirst, come to Me, come and share
    The living waters fair;
        For I will give
        To all who live
     Unending draughts of Love!"

O Deepest Wisdom, counting all things dross,
    Save love of us, so wretched and forlorn;
O Love Incarnate, counting gain for loss,
    Sharing our life, yet of the Spirit born;
Uplifted to embrace us on the Cross,
    Love spared You not, Your hands with nails were torn,
    Enduring Pilate's scorn,
        That dreadful Day,
        Our debt to pay,
     Upon Your Cross of Love!

For see, how Wisdom hid herself away,
    And Love alone was to our vision plain:
Omnipotence sat shrouded on that Day,
    When strength and power were turned to bitter pain;
No gift but Love upon that Altar lay,
    Love, that for us was spent, for us was slain,
    Power and will were vain;
        Love crucified,
        Fettered and tied,
     Embraced mankind for Love.

Then Jesus, if I be inebriate,
   Enamoured of Your sweetness and Your woe,
From all reproach I stand inviolate,
   Though foolish and distracted I should grow;
You too were bound by Love, Who was so great,
   That He was strong to bring Your greatness low;
   Nor would I scatheless go,
      Though all amazed,
      My wits be dazed,
   With Your caress, O Love.

For that same Love, that drives me all distraught,
   Took all Your Wisdom, Lord, amazingly;
That Love, that dips in langour all my thought,
   Destroyed Your powers too, and all for me:
And I will keep back nothing; I am caught
   By Love Himself: I yield, I would not flee;
   O let my sentence be
      For Love to die,
      No succour nigh,
   O grant me death, my Love.

Love, Love, of naught but Love my tongue can sing,
   Your wounded Hand has pierced my heart so deep:
Love, Love, with You made one, with You I cling,
   Upon Your breast, my Jesus, let me sleep;
Love, Love, with love my heart is perishing;
   Love, like an Eagle snatching me Your sheep,
   For You I swoon, I weep,
      Love, let me be,
      Entirely,
   Your own in death, O Love!